DEMOS

D1635574

Demos is an independent think tank committed to radical thinking on the long-term problems facing the UK and other advanced industrial societies.

It aims to develop ideas – both theoretical and practical – to help shape the politics of the twenty-first century, and to improve the breadth and quality of political debate.

Demos publishes books and a regular journal and undertakes substantial empirical and policy oriented research projects. Demos is a registered charity.

In all its work Demos brings together people from a wide range of backgrounds in business, academia, government, the voluntary sector and the media to share and cross-fertilise ideas and experiences.

For further information and subscription details please contact:

Demos
Panton House
25 Haymarket
London SW1Y 4EN
Telephone: 0171 321 2200
Facsimile: 0171 321 2342
email: mail@demos.co.uk

Other publications available from Demos:

Civic Entrepreneurship
The Creative City
Park Life
Tomorrow's Politics

To order a publication or
a free catalogue please contact Demos.

Creating wealth
from waste

Robin Murray

DEM☉S

First published in 1999 by
Demos
Panton House
25 Haymarket
London SW1Y 4EN
Telephone: 0171 321 2200
Facsimile: 0171 321 2342
email: mail@demos.co.uk

ISBN 1 898309 07 8
Printed in Great Britain by BDW Associates
Design by Lindsay Nash

Contents

Acknowledgments

This book is the result of joint work over the past three years on a project on the employment potential of the new waste economy. The project came about as the result of a request from the London Planning Advisory Committee to consider their long term waste strategy in the light of recycling experience elsewhere. They were interested in the extent to which recycling could deliver on a number of aspects of their planning policies on sustainability, particularly in terms of air quality, CO_2 reduction, resource saving, the re-industrialisation of run down areas of London, as well as the creation of jobs. This work overlapped with the Demos Working Cities project, whose aim was to develop a new approach to job creation through influencing the way changes take place in 'productive systems'. Waste was an example of a productive system, spanning households, councils, governments and a range of industrial and service sectors, and was on a the point of a major change.

The work in London involved the creation of a consortium of 28 London boroughs to develop an intensive recycling programme, and a number of other bodies to 'animate' the change. In the past six months similar work has been undertaken with a consortium of eleven district authorities in Essex to develop a 60 per cent recycling and composting waste plan. The London work was written up in *Re-Inventing Waste*, Ecologika, 1998. The present book develops themes from these studies in relation to wider national issues.

The approach adopted in each of these cases was to invite Canadian specialists with experience of running intensive recycling schemes and related enterprises overseas to work with UK local authorities. Five have played a central and continuing role: Keith Collins and Kathy Killinger, who shaped the argument as presented and who are responsible for many of the ideas, figures and all the graphs; Bob Argue and Cheryl Nash, who developed some of the most innovative schemes in Canada and were *inter alia* responsible for the model of UK waste composition and CO_2 emissions which are summarised in the first part; and Jack McGinnis who has been one of the great pioneers of the new waste economy in North America and who has provided invaluable strategic and practical advice.

At this end the work has involved many people and friends. I am particularly indebted to Worku Lakew, Nicky Gavron, Deborah Sacks, Alan Watson and Andy Moore, to Tom Bentley, Lindsay Nash and other colleagues at Demos, and to my wife Frances Murray, and daughters Marika and Beth, who exemplify one of the themes of this book, namely the close inter-relation of the formal and informal economies.

London
June 1999

Preface

Around the world, the natural environment is becoming a primary driver of political action and behavioural change. Morally and politically, it is almost impossible to deny the power of Green logic. Population growth and growing resource use have put the basic conditions that support our existence at risk, disrupting climate, weather, oceans and food production, and costing ever more in human, economic and environmental terms.

As a result, Green rhetoric is being universally adopted. No politician can publicly deny the importance of environmental action, yet few political systems have delivered the change that most citizens would like to see. Surveys have repeatedly shown that most people feel little sense of agency and surprisingly little trust in governments to deliver real progress. Environment is a classic example of a policy field that infuses all others, where the targets and language are easy to adopt but achieving them is much harder. It requires us to change most of what we do and most of the institutions we rely on, often all at the same time. For governments, this seems even harder in an age of globalisation, when their powers are thought to be dwindling in the face of technological change and international capital markets.

This book shows how radical environmental progress can be achieved by changing one of our most universal and mundane activities: the way we empty our bins. The solutions it presents are very simple: developing new household habits and using new materials like plastic boxes for doorstep collection. But the systems needed to make it work at the right scale are far more complex. The experience of creating them in practice, which the author and his colleagues have been engaged in for the past three years, provides lessons that extend far beyond waste: to the role of business, the structure of government and the relationship between the local and global economies.

Recycling is one of those activities that everybody supports in principle, but in the UK it has failed to take off. In 1995, the government set a target of 25 per cent recycled household waste by the millennium. Since then the rate has risen by just 2 per cent to a miserable 8 per cent. If everybody supports the idea, what has gone wrong? The explanation lies in the way that different parts of the overall system have failed to combine and in a victory of short over long-term thinking. Instead of a competition between state and market, the solution lies in understanding the role of the *productive system* – all those agents and institutions involved in producing a particular good, whether warmth, light, food, or clean streets – as a whole.

This way of thinking – which emphasises the intelligence and potential for innovation spread across a whole system, rather than the concentration of power and knowledge at the top – can be found in two spheres of society that, at first sight, seem like strange bedfellows. They are the leading edge of the knowledge economy, with its emphasis on networks, collaboration and creativity, and the emerging global movement of Greens, community enterprise and local economic development, which exemplifies innovative capacity, self-reliance and sustainability. Between them they are helping to shape a new path for capitalism, set out in agenda-setting books such as *Factor Four* and *Natural Capitalism*, which show how radical changes in resource and material productivity can improve long-term business prospects *and* achieve real environmental progress.

These shared characteristics point to a way through one of the most difficult conundrums of Green politics. While many people want to be involved in creating environmental solutions, most organised environmental action still seems to take place at the margins of the economic and political systems. While mass participation is growing, it is usually in the form of protest: against incinerators, roads or the treatment of animals. The most dedicated or radical environmentalists may create alternatives but hardly ever on a scale that can compete with established business or government practice. At the same time, global industries will not be persuaded to build sustainability into their operations until social and environmental costs – currently referred to as 'externalities' – can be accounted for within their profit and loss. This problem can be overcome by creating systems that can combine the decentralised diversity of community enterprise with the scale and pace of international markets. This book explains how that link can be made.

In particular, four key lessons emerge from the analysis. First, this approach creates new opportunities for local economic development. Because waste management is necessarily a local phenomenon, solutions that focus on waste as a productive resource create virtuous economic cycles by feeding resources back into the local economy, even where it is linked to international markets, for example in recycled paper or aluminium. For a whole range of goods and services that are mainly produced in close proximity to their consumers – care, learning, waste, health, warmth and so on – this means that jobs and firms can be rooted in local areas and yet still be productive and competitive.

Second, labour-intensive systems can also be smarter and more productive than centralised, capital-intensive alternatives. Intensive recycling programmes depend on an army of workers, volunteers and household participators acting in concert to produce multiple streams of waste that can be fed back into the economy as a resource. The book estimates that developing such programmes across the UK could create up to 70,000 jobs. At a time when the conventional wisdom declares that governments can no longer create jobs using macroeconomic levers, this is profoundly important. Because they are both practical and knowledge intensive, combining manual work and information management, the kind of 'Green collar' jobs created also point to a new tier of high-quality employment that can help replace traditional manufacturing and industrial jobs.

Third, we need better systems for measuring different kinds of outcome. As well as the economic effects of recycling, it can create social and environmental dividends that contribute to quality of life and healthy communities. But these qualities, despite being policy goals for governments across the world, are rarely figured into economic planning or environmental regulation. As a result, the commercial incentives for investment create perverse outcomes and have led firms, local authorities and central government to move towards incineration and conclude that recycling is an expensive and inherently limited form of activity. This will only change when we can account properly for the varied effects of our different choices. Across the whole of society, business is gaining a new role in producing social and environmental outcomes. Until we can measure this contribution properly, we will not find a sustainable way of managing or regulating the economy.

Fourth, creating wealth from waste involves consumers and house-holders as active participants in the system and points to a new form of citizenship as a result. The idea that production and consumption are being re-united through individuals' experience is now spreading widely, having been first predicted in the late 1960s and 1970s. In areas where it produces social, public and environmental goods, we can see how such activity creates a new relationship between the individual and the state: practical, active and localised, a form of direct connec-tion that gives people the opportunity to make a difference, and ensures that the whole of what they do is greater than the sum of its parts. Again, at a time of widespread voter disaffection, this has huge significance.

But achieving the potential of all these areas demands a new role from government. Rather than controlling or managing such activity from the centre, public authorities must shape, guide and stimulate it. Instead of policing the boundary between public and private sectors, they must be able to take a broad view across the whole system, and help structure markets and incentives towards productive long-term change. This cannot be done solely from the bunkers of Whitehall and without a readiness to nurture innovation and take some risks along the way. One of the key qualities of business leaders in the most successful knowledge enterprises is that they recognise that innova-tion cannot take place under conditions of strict control. The knowl-edge, expertise and potential that exists across a whole system cannot be regulated or controlled from one source, and so harnessing them depends on the distribution of responsibility and accountability right across the field of activity.

It is also striking how the knowledge and evidence presented in this book was created not by traditional research or analysis but from prac-tice: the experience of innovation and failure, of adapting to local conditions and of watching real people test out the alternatives. This is a model of knowledge creation that government will increasingly have to embrace.

These are huge challenges. But evidence from around the world shows that they can be met and that the long-term benefits are enormous. In that sense, waste is a barometer for wider choices in the UK: whether we can embrace a new approach to developing our social and economic potential, or whether we are genuinely constrained by the structures and assumptions of the past. The opportunity, as this book shows, is surely too good to waste.

Tom Bentley
Director, Demos

Part I. Out of the wasteland

What are the roots that clutch, what branches grow
Out of this stony rubbish?

TS Eliot, *The Wasteland*

1. Beyond the dustbin

Waste has always been the shadow side of the economy. In production and consumption, it is that which is rejected as useless and barren. Whatever the word (garbage, rubbish, refuse, waste), and whichever the language, the meaning is similar. The social task of waste management has been to get rid of it. Today's waste is carried away through sewers and dustbins, dispatched in the air through burning, dumped in disused quarries or the oceans, onto middens or fly-tipped in gutters or behind hedges.

In the UK alone, 435 million tonnes of waste is disposed of every year. The household dustbin accounts for only 6 per cent of the total. Eight per cent is sewage sludge, 36 per cent comes from the commercial and industrial sectors and half is produced by primary industries like mining, quarrying, dredging and farming. In the words of the anthropologist Mary Douglas, it represents matter in the wrong place.

Farms and quarries use waste as a resource. Farmers spread muck on their fields. Quarriers use rubble to landscape the land they have blasted. But for most industries and households, waste has to be collected, transported and tipped. This has been the basis for waste as a sector of the economy.

Where there has been muck, there has always been money. In the waste heaps and streets of nineteenth century and twentieth century London, as in those of the third world today, it has been a sector of scavengers, of Steptoes and their sons, of car breakers yards and scrap merchants. The steel mills have provided a steady outlet for scrap. Rags have been the basis for factories making reconstituted cloth and felting. Even food scraps found a use. Until the early 1970s much of the organic waste from London was used to feed pigs in East Anglia. Tottenham became famous for its recycled sausages.

That which could not be recycled was largely landfilled. By the early 1990s there were 4,077 registered landfill sites in Britain, accounting for over 90 per cent of unrecycled waste. Landfill was primarily a small firm business (like its sister industry, the funeral sector) made up of local operators with empty holes to sell.

This can hardly be called an industry. It is a low technology, labour intensive service, marginalised by the nature of its trade and traditions, working at the margins of health regulations and below the radar line of the stockmarket. In local government, waste management has been a low status occupation, not a career path for aspiring chief executives or aspiring politicians. Waste only hits the headlines when things go wrong. Economically and politically, as the Latin origin (*vastus*) of its name implies, waste is a desert.

The new economy of waste

All of this is now changing. Three basic drivers of change are turning waste and waste management into a dynamic, fast-changing, international economic sector. This transformation presents new choices and opportunities, and provides lessons and pointers for industrial, social and environmental policy in the new post-industrial landscape. The drivers of a change are:

- growing concern about the hazards of waste disposal
- broader environmental concerns, especially global warming and resource depletion
- economic opportunities created by new waste regulations and technological innovation.

Waste and hazards

In the UK, officially designated hazardous waste has increased by 50 per cent over the past decade to 4.5 million tonnes a year (this does not include nuclear waste). Awareness of the dangers of 'non-hazardous' waste has also grown. Landfill sites for example, because of their methane emissions, are a significant cause of global warming and a source of ground water pollution.

Incinerators also produce hazards. Their emissions of acid gases, mercury, dioxins and furans have led to widespread protests in North America, Japan and continental Europe, forcing the closure of plants and the abandonment of plans for new ones.[1] Several North American states and provinces have now banned new incinerators.

In Japan, a 1997 stockbroker's survey found that only eight of the 1,500 operating incinerators met international dioxin standards, with one of them emitting 10,000 times the concentrations allowed elsewhere. In Germany, 1 million people signed petitions against incinerators. In France, a government survey of incinerator emissions in 1998 led to the closure of twenty incinerators and probation for others. Concern was further heightened by high dioxin levels in milk produced near an incinerator north of Paris and, in another case, by radioactive materials in incinerator waste. In the UK, recent epidemiological studies found abnormal rates of cancer for people living near incinerators and, most recently in Derbyshire, near landfills. Such studies have awakened awareness of the hazards of waste.[2]

This is partly a new awareness of old dangers, for example of methane from organic waste. But it also reflects the increased toxicity of materials in the modern waste stream. Paints, batteries, motor oil, aerosols, solvents, fridges with their CFCs, are all potential pollutants. Many of the new materials become toxic when incinerated. Burning releases dioxins from plastics and toxic flame retardants from TVs, computers and textiles. Waste scares, like food scares, are generating a new environmental politics.

In the nineteenth century a new sanitary order was established because of the threat of disease. Today, waste has re-emerged as a political issue because of the threat of toxicity.

Earth and air

The second driver of change is concern about global warming and resource depletion. In 1900 the United States consumed 200 million tonnes of materials. By 1945 this rose to 600 million tonnes, and by the late 1980s to 2,600 million tonnes, out of world consumption of 16 billion tonnes. There is now widespread recognition that this level of consumption, along with the energy required and the greenhouse gases produced by it, is unsustainable.[3]

The effort to reduce consumption of primary materials and the energy needed to produce them has focused on five industries – paper, steel, aluminium, plastics and container glass – which account for 31 per cent of manufacturing energy use in the United States. The US Environmental Protection Agency recently estimated that a 1 per cent increase in recycling in the US would reduce carbon dioxide emissions by an amount equivalent to taking 1.2 million cars off the road. By 1998 the US recycling rate had reached 31.5 per cent, compared with 8 per cent in 1990. This is the equivalent of a reduction of 28 million cars.

As environmental concerns came to the fore in the 1990s, all roads led to waste. From centuries of obscurity, the waste industry found itself at the hub of environmental argument. The main response by governments was to strengthen environmental and waste regulation. The Germans passed an ordnance to reduce packaging and increase taxes in 1991. Denmark put taxes on waste disposal. The EU tightened up on incinerator emissions, negotiated agreement to a radical reduction in landfill and introduced a community-wide directive to cut packaging waste in 1995. While the international trend in economic policy was to reduce regulations and cut taxes, waste has been subjected to ever tighter regulations and higher taxes.

Waste and the economy
The third driver of change is economic. New opportunities were created by regulatory change – in waste management, in recycling and in the use of the recycled materials. The world of municipal collection, small firm disposal and the rag-and-bone man suddenly came into contact with a wider economy.

Multinationals are taking an increasing interest in waste. Privatisation has opened up new markets in collection. The new standards of treatment and the industrialisation of waste management require resources beyond the means of small and medium-sized firms. A 420,000 tonnes incinerator now requires an investment of £125 million. A typical waste incineration contract over 25 years costs £1 billion, once recycling, composting, residual landfilling and the return on investment are taken into account.[4] This is big money, which requires big firms.

As a result, there have been a wave of takeovers and expansion. In Britain there were 420 recorded takeovers of waste firms between

1990 and 1998. UK waste management is now dominated by seven majors: three American, two French, one Australian and one British. Four of the top five are owned by water companies. Other large firms are being attracted into the recycling sector, some of them are processors looking for materials, others are applying recognition and sorting technologies to recycling.

The opportunities for waste processors are particularly significant. Faced with diminishing primary resources and tighter regulation of energy use, major industrial sectors have been shifting their sources of supply from virgin to secondary materials.

A typical example is paper. Global consumption of paper and board has risen from 46 million tonnes in 1950 to 253 million tonnes in 1993. The Food and Agriculture Organisation (FAO) forecasts that it will rise to 479 million tonnes by 2010, a tenfold increase in 60 years. This has already led to the destruction of natural forests and to the growth of plantation forestry, which creates problems for biodiversity, acidification, erosion and water supply. The FAO estimates that no more than two-fifths of the growth in paper consumption can be accommodated from virgin wood. Even this will mean increased transport distances, new hydro-electric schemes and further pressure on natural forests. For the remaining 60 per cent, the FAO sees recycling as the only option.[5]

In the past ten years the paper industry has been transformed by these necessities. Improvements in de-inking technology have cut costs so that, in Germany, France and Britain, it is now 35 per cent cheaper to produce newsprint from recycled paper than from virgin pulp. Germany recycles the greatest amount of paper – 71 per cent – while Europe as a whole has reached 50 per cent. In North America the proportion of old paper and board recycled has risen from a third to a half during the 1990s. Overall, there has been a dramatic shift from mills located near virgin forests (in Scandinavia and Northern Canada) to those near concentrations of used paper in major cities and towns.

This story is being repeated in other industries. Foundries for aluminium auto parts are using recycled cans, and new can recycling plants are appearing each year. Glass factories can now use up to 90 per cent recycled inputs and new technologies are emerging for recycling electronics and plastics.

In short, the environmental movement has created a new economic interest in waste and recycling. This interest, combined with the opportunities created by technological innovation, is extending down through the supply chain.

A new competition between nations

These changes offer a new basis for international competitiveness in the global economy. Rather than seeing resource constraints and tighter regulation as a brake on economic growth, governments are beginning to recognise that the emerging 'secondary materials' economy and 'eco-efficiency' offer opportunities to stimulate innovation and create new sources of wealth and jobs.

The pioneers of advanced national environmental regimes will generate technologies that can be exported, especially once the new regulatory regimes are adopted internationally. But where governments have traditionally sought to promote and protect individual technologies and companies, it is now whole systems of regulation and production that matter most.

This strategy is an explicit goal of German economic policy. The federal government has introduced strong, and often high cost, environmental legislation, which gave its recycling, packaging, chemical and processing industries a competitive edge when the same regulatory standards came to be extended throughout the EU.

The US government has also recognised this opportunity. Warren Christopher, Secretary of State during the early 1990s, promoted a strategy to use 'environmental initiatives to promote larger strategic and economic goals ... helping our environmental sector capture a larger share of a $400 billion global market.'[6] Canada has also realised that it needs to shift from its historical role as a primary material producer to a specialist second materials economy. In 1990 Japan produced a 100-year plan for developing high technology solutions to the sustainability challenge, which was reflected in its strategic programme for the waste industry.[7]

Waste and the economy are now bound together, as in a double helix. Waste should no longer seen as a cost and an economic drain on productive resources. It has become a source of innovation. Like energy, it is contributing to a profound restructuring of the international economy.

In managing this process, public policy has a central place. Whereas previous waves of innovation have been generated from within the economy, the environmental re-direction of the economy – because it deals with costs external to the market – is driven by politics and government.

This book explores the social and economic opportunities created during economic transitions. Waste is at a historical turning point, but this does not mean that its path of development is fixed in advance. Transitions can take place in different forms and follow different courses. The second function of public policy in this context is not just to facilitate the transition but to shape it in a way that meets wider policy goals. The next chapter sets out the choices we currently face in the direction of modernisation in the management of waste.

2. Alternative modernisations

The old waste order is now dying. No one in the waste industry, in government, in municipalities, let alone in the environmental movement can be found to argue in its favour. But it is not yet clear what will replace it. Green principles have been overwhelmingly adopted in reports and at conferences. Green language has provided a shared vocabulary – sustainability, waste minimisation, recycling, from waste to resource, closed loops, the proximity principle. But, partly because it has been adopted so widely, the Green discourse masks differences over the direction of change. This chapter sets out alternatives paths of modernisation that have been adopted elsewhere in response to the waste challenge and explains the differences between them.

Two main courses have been followed. The first – chemico-energy modernisation – seeks to control the hazards of waste disposal by applying modern technology to the old waste system, and recover chemical materials and energy through the disposal process. The second – eco-modernisation – aims to increase resource productivity and reduce hazards through the *design* of products and processes, and by lengthening the life of materials through recycling. The first applies modern technology to the process of destruction, the second to that of conservation. There is a major conflict between these two approaches that has determined the politics of waste in the advanced industrial countries in the 1990s. The UK currently stands at a crossroads between the two.

Chemico-energy modernisation
This approach applies the techniques of power generation and the chemical industry to the handling of waste. Waste is collected in the

traditional way, as a single stream of mixed materials that are then taken to a treatment plant, usually an incinerator.

Waste incinerators are not new: they were first developed in the late nineteenth century and became the main means of disposal in some European and North American cities in the early twentieth century, until their costs rose above those of landfill. A number of countries that were unsuited for landfill (Japan, the Netherlands, Denmark, Switzerland) came to burn the majority of their household waste. Others, such as some US states, looked to incineration in the late 1980s when landfill shortages were forecast.

What is new is the attempt by incinerator producers to respond to the devastating findings of the environmental effects of the process. When burning was found to be a major polluter and to set free hazardous substances, the incinerator manufacturers raised the temperature at which waste was burnt and introduced more effective precipitators, scrubbers, additives and filters to catch or immobilise hazardous substances before they were emitted to the air.

The pace of change can be judged from Figure 1. In 1989 the EU introduced a tighter set of emission standards, which led to widespread closure and upgrading of incinerators all over Europe. The revised directive based new limits on the level of German technology in the early 1990s. But during the 1990s technology advanced so that already

Figure 1. Emission limit values in Europe (in mg/m3)

Substance	Current ELVs	EU proposals	Dutch ELVs	German best permitted practice
Dust	30	10/30	5	0.05 - 5/5-30
Volatile Organic Carbon	20	10	-	1 - 5
Carbon Monoxide	100	50	na	na
Sulphur Dioxide	300	50/200	40	1.3 - 15/25
Oxides of Nitrogen	350	200	70	40/200
Hydrogen Chloride	30	10	10	0.3 - 5
Hydrogen Fluoride	2	1	1	.05 - 0.5
Cadmium	0.1	0.05	0.05	0.0002 - 0.005
Mercury	0.1	0.05	0.05	0.0001 0.02
Dioxins & Furans (ng/m3)	1	0.1	0.01-0.1	0.001 - .05
Total heavy metals	1	0.5	1	0.004 - 0.1

Sources: London Waste Ltd and European Environment Bureau

the Dutch have been able to raise standards further, while the best German technology has cut emissions broadly by a factor of ten. Significantly, it is the nuclear industry – facing over-capacity in the wake of a reduction in nuclear power plants – that has played a part in the upgrading of mixed waste incineration.

As a technology, incineration is about the management of hazards and the disposal of materials. The main thrust of technical developments is destruction and control. Of the 780 incinerators in the UK in the early 1990s, 700 dealt with clinical waste, 40 were attached to chemical companies, six burnt sewage sludge and four specialised in hazardous waste. The remaining 30 were designed for municipal waste. After the tightening of emission controls, the overall number fell to 110, of which six were municipal and 104 were geared explicitly to managing hazards. Pollution control constitutes a major proportion of the cost, technological capacity and space requirement of an incinerator.[8]

In addition, incineration produces energy and has led some governments (and environmentalists) to see it as a contributor to sustainable energy production. However, this is a by-product. Mixed waste incinerators are inefficient energy producers: only 20 per cent of the energy generated by the waste is usually captured.

Another technology now being developed is pyrolysis, where organic waste is burnt at relatively low temperatures to produce char (like charcoal), oils and combustible gases. The oils can be used as a chemical feedstock and as fuel. Feedstock includes mixed waste, plastics, tyres and sewage sludge.

Essentially, pyrolysis involves chemically 'mining' waste to produce elements that can be used for energy generation or chemical inputs.[9] Anaerobic digestion, which is designed to capture the methane from the degradation of organic waste for use as fuel or a chemical feedstock, is a more limited example.

From the viewpoint of existing waste management systems, the advantage of incinerators is that the system can continue as before. Compactor vehicles pick up mixed waste from households, factories and offices. Waste treatment is located on centralised, specialist sites, for which long-term contracts can be arranged. The structure of the waste profession is unaltered and innovation is provided by machinery suppliers. For large centralised institutions – governments, waste companies and machinery suppliers – these are often decisive advantages.

But incinerators now evoke levels of opposition similar to nuclear power. The main reason is the health and environmental impacts of emissions. Because the input of municipal incinerators is mixed waste, it is difficult to control the hazardous elements within it. The combustion process itself also sets free hazardous substances such as dioxins. The policy response to air contamination and toxicity during the 1990s has been to tighten standards, prompting the upgrade of the incineration process.

But there remains an inherent problem. As long as the materials being burnt are hazardous or are made so by combustion, the plant itself will be a potential hazard. Reducing the toxics entering the air cannot help but drive them back to the ground through deposits in the ash. Attention is now being turned to lightening regulation of the ash (see Figure 2).

Like other chemical plants, incinerators are subject to accidents and the loss of emissions control. Two of the most modern incinerators in Britain, the upgraded Edmonton and SELCHP in south London, reported 183 emissions infringements between 1995 and 1998. Monitoring and controlling the general levels of emissions becomes more expensive as the standards are raised. In short, incineration is a technology of the previous industrial era. It carries an inherent tension between internal and external costs. It is inflexible. It is inefficient both as a disposal option and as an energy generator. It leads not to material conservation and hazard reduction but material destruction and hazard creation.

Figure 2. Elements of leachate in residues from municipal incinerators

Elements of Leachate	EU proposal	Bottom ash I	Bottom ash II	Fly ash/gas cleaning residues
Chloride	50	530	610-950	3,445
Zinc	0.3	0.4	0.08 - 0.12	1.8
Lead	0.03	1.2	< 0.02 -0.65	36
Cadmium	0.01	< 0.06	< 0.012	0.01

Source: Ends Report 27, July 1997

This is why incinerators have been hard to site. In the US, 248 new municipal incinerators have been blocked and the number still in operation has fallen from 170 in 1991 to 119 in 1998. In Ontario, Canada, incinerators were banned. In Germany a number of Lander have banned incinerators because of public feeling against them, while in Denmark there is a move to reduce dependence on incineration despite the infrastructure investment already made. In France, the environment minister has written to municipalities advising them to reduce their plans for new incinerators. In the UK, municipal proposals for incinerators, have met with extensive opposition. The Essex waste plan (opening the way to substantial incineration) received 10,000 objections. A Medway proposal to build an incinerator generated 15,000 objections. Hampshire has been blocked in its incineration proposals by public opposition, and campaigns are currently being undertaken in Kidderminster, Portsmouth and Bexley.

Eco-modernisation

An alternative path has unfolded during the 1990s. It stresses economy of resource use and the safety of materials. This is a simple proposition, but its effects can be so far-reaching and dramatic that it arguably constitutes the beginning of a new 'post-industrial' era. Its aim is to redesign the whole system of material flows, in order to eliminate waste and disposal. Companies and whole industries are pursuing zero waste programmes. Japanese car makers have now reached 85 per cent recyclability and are targeting 90 per cent by 2000. Honda Canada, whose Ontario plant produces 167,000 cars a year, recently received an award for cutting its waste by 97 percent to two kilograms per vehicle.

Chemico-energy modernisation uses simple flows and complex treatments and, like the current waste regime in Britain, is organised around the stages of disposal (collection, treatment, disposal). Waste minimisation through eco-modernisation, on the other hand, depends on complex flows and simple or specialist treatment. It is organised around material streams and creates a circular flow of separate materials as an alternative to the linear flow of mass waste. Its central concept is the 'closed loop'.

As a result, the innovations of eco-modernisation are in collection systems rather than high tech plants. The cost of collection and sorting has been one of the main barriers to increasing recycling among households and small traders. Picking up the scraps from a steel mill is much simpler than recovering the 2 to 3 billion cans in Britain's domestic dustbins. The challenge facing recyclers is therefore similar to that worked on by Toyota, Benetton and modern supermarkets. If the items being processed or produced are many and diverse, rather than uniform (as they were in Henry Fords original twentieth century manufacturing system), how can the economies of the production or processing line be retained?

Toyota's re-invention of the assembly line was inspired by seeing an American supermarket and the model is relevant to recycling. Like retailers, recyclers are using containers, multi-purpose vehicles, bar codes and central warehouses to increase both the specialisation and the efficiency of their systems. Where supermarkets organise themselves to distribute the widest range of products from the supplier to the warehouse to the shop to the individual household, recycling runs in reverse.

The three stages of eco-modernisation

The starting point for recycling systems is where retailing ends: the household. Intensive recycling requires householders to separate their waste into three main streams: organics, dry recyclables and residual waste, supplemented by periodic collections of a fourth stream of durable goods and hazardous items. The technology is in the logistics and in the various elements needed to make this complex collection system work effectively. Recycling needs skilled frontline collectors, transformed management information systems[10] and multiple bins. Looking through the patent register in this field, it is striking how many refer to new types of dustbin: bins that breathe, that have compartments and/or wheels, that hook onto others, that go under the sink or behind the door. One of the earliest 'inventions' was a simple plastic blue box in which householders were asked to place their dry recyclables. Invented in Canada, this box is now used by 50 million households in North America. By skilful arrangement, some recycling schemes pick up 21 separated materials from in and around a blue box.

Collection provides the link between the household and the re-processor. The methods and skills used determine the quantity and the quality of recovered material. They will determine its environmental impact and its cost. Once separated, baled and dispatched, the next stage of the process lies with the manufacturers. The processing sectors have the specialist knowledge to convert recovered materials into useable inputs: how to take ink off old newsprint or recover tin from tin cans. Increased recovery of materials generates innovations downstream: reconverting materials and developing new products that can use the materials. These innovations are the second stage in the closed loop.

The third stage is design. Some materials are expensive or impossible to recycle. Recyclers curse multi-layer packaging (like Tetrapaks) and disposable nappies (which account for nearly 4 per cent of UK household waste or 730,000 tonnes a year). Some recyclers refuse to pick up plastics because it is so expensive to recycle. As a result, pressure is pushed back up the stream to redesign these items or to provide substitutes.

Some products, like consumer durables, are necessarily complex. They can be redesigned to lengthen their lives and to ease recycling. For example, car and electronic manufacturers have simplified the plastics they use. Some computer cases now contain no glues, paints or composites. Manufacturers have redesigned packaging for re-use, such as plastic crates and pallets, and designed machines so that modules can be replaced rather than the whole machine being scrapped.[11]

Design then moves further into minimising material. If the costs of waste are borne by those that produce it, there is a new incentive to reduce waste. The OECD estimates that even in current market conditions, firms can make profitable reductions in material (and energy) use of between 10 and 40 per cent.

There is a progression here, starting with the consumer as waste generator and then moving back up the pipe. The spotlight in this system is thrown on origins and destinations. The ink on the *Daily Mail* makes it difficult to recycle – why not change it? *New Scientist* uses paper made in Finland and partly sourced from Russian natural forests – why not use recycled? Could Coca Cola use returnable plastic bottles (which they do)? Can my fridge be made and maintained so that it lasts longer (which it can)? The goals of recyclability and making more with less become the driving forces of change within the system and are reinforced by increased consumer awareness of the reasons for change.[12]

The same progression applies to hazards. With source separation, hazardous items are kept apart and either recycled or disposed of as special waste. This is a first step, preventing their contamination of loads of mixed waste. One programme in Ontario reported the diversion of 5,800 tonnes of household hazardous waste in 1997. The waste included acids, anti-freeze, oils (27 per cent), paint (24 per cent), flammables (22 per cent), car batteries (13 per cent), propane tanks (5 per cent), inorganic cyanides, oxidisers, isocynates, pesticides, aerosols, dry cell batteries, oil filters, pharmaceuticals, cylinders and syringes. All of these would normally have all gone to landfill.

Hazards can then be tracked to their source and substituted through design. There have already been significant moves to replace synthetics with biodegradable materials made from plant starches, oils and enzymes. Vegetable oils are being used instead of mineral oils in paints and inks. Three quarters of US newspapers now use soya-based biodegradable inks. Starch and sugar are being used instead of petroleum in plastics. Enzymes have replaced phosphates in 90 per cent of all detergents in Europe. Switzerland has banned PVC drinking bottles and the Czech Republic has decided to remove all PVC from packaging by 2001. These examples are part of a 'cleaning up' of products and their process of production.

Contending modernities

These two approaches to modernisation in waste management are at odds with each other. They embody different organisational cultures, one representing the old industrial order, the other the new. It is striking that in the US the most advanced and innovative applications of recycling have come from leading edge areas of post-industrial production, California and Seattle. The issue is no longer the desirability of change. On virtually all scores: environmental impact, safety, long-term costs, innovation and employment, eco-modernisation is the preferred option. Yet some countries, particularly those depending on incinerators, have found it far harder to develop recycling systems than others.

For example, Japan, although a pioneer in materials reduction, has been unable to shift to intensive household recycling and instead is proposing to a new generation of incinerators. Yet this strategy is facing widespread opposition.

The pace of change

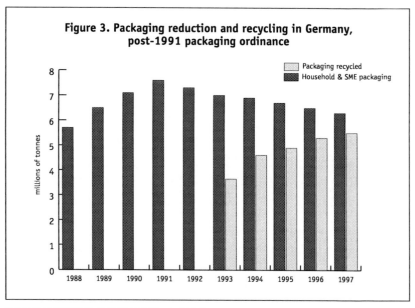

Figure 3. Packaging reduction and recycling in Germany, post-1991 packaging ordinance

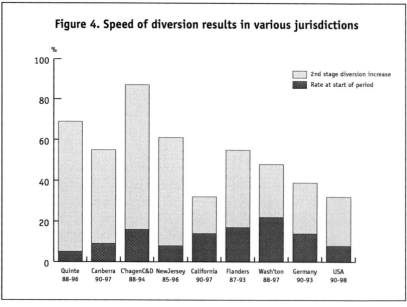

Figure 4. Speed of diversion results in various jurisdictions

Holland

The Dutch waste policy is part of a wider policy for resource economy and the reduction of pollution. Since 1985 Holland has cut its industrial pollution loads to air and water (except for CO_2 and Nox) by 50 to 70 per cent. By 2010 another halving of pollution loads is planned against production which will have doubled since 1985.

Overall material efficiency of environmentally sensitive inputs per unit of industrial production will have increased by at least a factor of four by 2010. The Dutch government estimates that 50 per cent of overall efficiency gains in energy consumption can be attributed to a more efficient use of materials.

The waste strategy has used very tight physical and financial constraints, financial incentives to improve life cycleproduct performance and producer responsibility legislation for the recycling and use of post-consumer waste. Holland already recycles 72 per cent of its waste, and by 2000 this will have risen to 75 per cent.

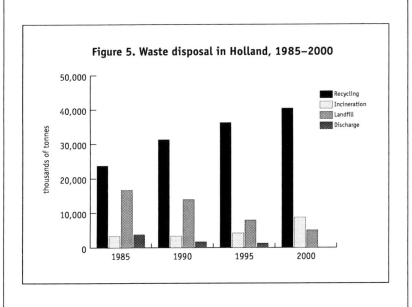

Figure 5. Waste disposal in Holland, 1985–2000

Switzerland, on the other hand, which had high levels of incineration, has made a successful transition to recycling and now has to *import* waste to feed their incinerators. The Swiss are now separating their waste into fifteen streams and recycle over 50 per cent of household waste. The same has happened in Germany, with many Lander now recycling over 50 per cent of their waste. Denmark, despite its sunk investment in domestic incinerators, is now shifting its strategy towards recycling. Its current recycling rate is 54 per cent with a proposed target of 64 per cent by 2004.

Creating systems change

If there is general agreement about the benefits of eco-modernisation, the question is how to bring it about. Intensive recycling and waste reduction depends on changing whole systems. It relies on distributed intelligence rather than centralised knowledge and on innovation that is widely dispersed across collection, processing, materials technology and product design. As a result, the change can seem far harder to achieve than the straightforward modernisation of existing systems.

This presents problems. How is the new system to be established? It cannot be set up like a disposal plant because it involves so many different players. How can the change best be triggered? How can it be financed if the gains from an innovation can only partially be captured by those who introduced it? What makes sense if everyone changes may not make sense if I do it on my own. Unlike information technology, there is no chip or piece of software that can be diffused and transform the system. Eco-production deals with de-materialisation and changes in flow across a wide range of sectors. Our current systems of patents, organisation and finance are not well suited to promote system economies of this kind.

Yet these characteristics, which are hard to create simultaneously, are the same ones that make it so potent an instrument for change. Where incineration is an increasingly costly technology, confined in its economic impact, and fails to tackle the root causes of waste hazards, eco-modernisation is part of a new post-industrial order. It shares many features with the emerging knowledge economy. It erodes traditional boundaries and demands new institutions. It is a motor of innovation and wealth creation. It is pervasive in its reach and profound in its impact.

For two centuries, time has been the core dynamic of industrial production: finding new ways to organise time has been the driver of economic progress since the first industrial revolution. Matter is now assuming an equivalent status to time, and applying intelligence to the way we treat and use materials is the great challenge of the next industrial revolution.

The rest of this book sets out how that change can be achieved in the secondary materials economy, and the benefits – environmental, economic, and social – that eco-modernisation can bring.

3. Environmental dividends

The London Borough of Haringey sends its waste to the UK's largest incinerator, located on its northern boundaries in Edmonton. The furnaces of Edmonton reduce Haringey's waste by 55 per cent, and the remainder is sent to a hazardous waste dump or to landfill in Essex.

In the age of zero waste, Edmonton is a dinosaur. Together with the other London incinerator in Lewisham, it accounts for substantial portions of toxic emissions in London from non-auto sources. Edmonton is third in the league of major industrial polluters in the UK. It has led to complaints from doctors of patients living on its windward side because of the incidence of asthma.

At the same time, the Borough of Haringey is pioneering a new type of recycling. It uses a small electric cart (PCV) which is hand operated and driven on the pavement. Its formal function is to recycle material and conserve primary resources. Each cart's daily collection of paper saves an estimated nineteen trees. But it also cuts back energy use and pollution. The paper is sent to the newly established £300 million Aylesford Newsprint plant in Kent. The environmental impact of recycling Haringey's paper at Aylesford is shown in Figure 6. On all except two of the criteria, recycling offers substantial reductions over incineration.

Similarly, the way Haringey collects its recyclables reinforces these savings. The cart embodies only an eighth of the material used to make a large waste vehicle. While a diesel collection vehicle does five miles to the gallon, the PCV runs on off peak electricity. The cost of a week's diesel would last the PCV for a year. Equally importantly, transferring collection off the roadway eases traffic and brings the collector closer

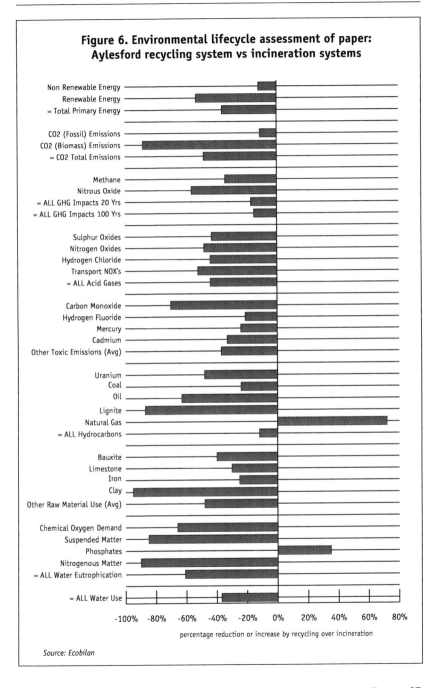

Figure 6. Environmental lifecycle assessment of paper: Aylesford recycling system vs incineration systems

Source: Ecobilan

to the public. So far there have been no complaints from pedestrians. In fact, people stop to talk about recycling. One of the recycling collectors even made the news when he stopped a mugging (see box on page 45).

Haringey illustrates the scope that recycling gives for addressing five central issues of sustainability currently facing government:

- greenhouse gas reduction
- sustainable energy
- resource depletion
- green cities
- rural sustainability.

Each of these has proved remarkably difficult to change.

Greenhouse gas reduction

The government's Climate Change Consultation Paper on reducing greenhouse gases (GHG) identified four strands of policy:

	Million tonnes of carbon equivalent (MTCE) per year
1. 10 per cent more energy from renewable sources	5.4
2. increased fuel duty	2–5
3. a package of home efficiency measures	2–4
4. afforestation	0.5
Total	*9–13.5*

The missing set of measures from this list is recycling. The US Environmental Protection Agency (EPA) has developed a model which shows that for every material recycled there are substantial GHG savings relative to landfill, and that for every tonne of a mixed basket of recyclables, 0.8 MTCE was saved, which is four times as much as by incineration.[13] Figure 7 shows the 1998 results of the US model by material. Using the EPA model and forecasts of materials recovered through intensive recycling in the UK, we estimate that recycling 70 per cent of recyclable domestic waste in the UK would save 14.8 million tonnes of carbon equivalent, which is more than the other four measures combined.

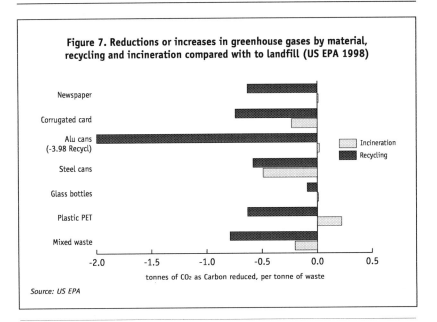

Figure 7. Reductions or increases in greenhouse gases by material, recycling and incineration compared with to landfill (US EPA 1998)

tonnes of CO₂ as Carbon reduced, per tonne of waste

Source: US EPA

Figure 8. United Kingdom CO₂ reduction through waste diversion

	no of households	CO2 reduction tonnes/year	Reduction per hshld tonnes/hshld	car equivalence @1,100l/year/car no of cars
25% diversion	24,600,000	6,660,000	0.271	2,421,818
50% diversion	24,600,000	11,050,000	0.449	4,018,182
70% diversion	24,600,000	14,800,000	0.602	5,381,818

Based on 10,000 miles per car per year, 1100 litres petrol per car per year, 2.5kg CO_2 reduction per litre

For local authorities, this creates the opportunity to contribute their share of CO_2 reductions by promoting intensive recycling programmes. They can also ensure that the recycling is carried out with vehicles and logistics that minimise the production of CO_2.

Sustainable energy

The government's sustainable energy policy has two elements: promoting energy efficient consumption (a so-called 'negawatt' strategy) and encouraging renewable energy sources. In the waste sector, the emphasis has been on the second element: sections of government have promoted incineration as a contribution to renewable energy production.

This fails to take account of the much larger savings in energy that accrue from recycling. On the one hand, mixed waste incineration is a low value producer of energy. Municipal waste has a low calorific value: only waste oils, solvents and plastics exceed the average value of available fuels (17kJ/kg) and these are the materials that create serious emission problems. The main UK incinerators also only produce power and do not capture heat, so that they achieve only 20 per cent efficiency. This is why the European Commission proposed in February 1999 that municipal incinerators be classed as disposal operations rather than as a means of energy recovery.

Recycling, on the other hand, creates industrial 'negawatts'. It substitutes already processed materials for energy intensive primary production and cuts energy requirements as a result. For example, a primary paper pulp mill consumes three to seven times more energy than a modern de-inking mill. As Figure 6 shows, the Aylesford plant uses one-third less energy in its lifecycle than the cycle of paper produced in a virgin paper mill in Sweden and then incinerated.

The net savings are even more striking in aluminium, but also apply to steel, glass, tyres and textiles. The re-treading of tyres, (of which there are 35 million discarded in the UK every year) saves 90 per cent of the energy embodied in the original tyre, and truck tyres can be re-treaded three or four times. In textiles, the Energy Efficiency Office found that the energy saving of a 100 per cent recycled wool textile compared with new wool was almost 50 per cent.[14]

For these reasons, a recycling programme such as that in Haringey should be a significant part of any sustainable energy strategy.[15]

Resource depletion

Recycling and re-use reduce the pressure on primary resources. In some sectors, such as machinery, cars and household appliances, there has been a long-term practice of scrap recycling, but substantial amounts are still landfilled, along with precious metals and other materials in electronic goods. Potential material savings from household waste are discussed in the next chapter. There are 9 million tonnes of organics, 8.3 million of dry recyclables and only 3 million of residual waste, some of which in due course can also be reduced or recycled.[16] Much of this material can be captured in the first two stages of intensive recycling: 7.4 million tonnes of organics, 3.3 million tonnes of paper, 1.2 million tonnes of glass, 670,000 tonnes of plastics, 440,000 tonnes of cans and 350,000 tonnes of textiles. If commercial and industrial waste was added, the figures would be substantially higher.

Take paper as an example. Paper can be recycled five or six times over. In 1998 the UK consumed 12.5 million tonnes, of which 59 per cent was imported, largely as virgin fibre paper. The paper industry estimates that the UK has the largest stock of unrecycled waste paper in western Europe, over 5 million tonnes. If the UK were able to raise its rate of recycling to German levels it would be equivalent to planting (or saving) 62.7 million trees per year.

Green cities

One of the principles of the new 'Green waste' regime is that people, firms and governments should take responsibility for the waste they produce. This is one reason for EU measures controlling the trans-border shipment of waste and for the Basle Ban of 1994, which prevents the export of waste to developing countries. There have also been moves to apply this principle to cities and regions. For example, SERPLAN (the regional planning body for the South-east of England) has decided that its member counties, including London, should be self-sufficient in their treatment of 'non-inert' waste by the 'earliest practicable date'.

Self-sufficiency poses a major challenge to cities. Few have access to landfill. If, as SERPLAN envisages, self-sufficiency were to be achieved by expanding incineration, this threatens a number of other environmental policies and leaves cities with the problem of disposing of residual ash. This is why the London Planning Body (LPAC) decided to interpret self-sufficiency differently and proposed a strategy of intensive recycling.

The motive – as has often been the case with recycling – was in part defensive. But LPAC found that recycling not only avoided the environmental costs of new incinerators but also contributed to other urban environmental challenges.[17] The four most applicable to other towns and cities are: air quality, reduced traffic, high-rise estates and litter.

Air quality

Incineration, largely an urban phenomenon, has a profound and negative impact on air quality. For example, the Tyseley incinerator in Birmingham was identified as the second worst polluter in a 1999 Environmental Agency league table. Edmonton was third. The Nottingham Eastcroft incinerator registered eleven unauthorised releases during 1996–97, mainly of hydrogen chloride and oxides of nitrogen.

Another complaint from residents of these areas is of increased asthma. This has been linked to significant emissions of dust. In 1996 the Edmonton plant emitted 263 tonnes of particulates into London's air and it proposes to increase this by a further 21 tonnes if it is allowed to expand.[18] The extension alone would add emissions equivalent to an estimated 262 million diesel car kilometre equivalents, or some 50,000 diesel cars driven daily for an hour in London, as well as the new diesel traffic generated by the plant (a minimum of 32,500 heavy diesel vehicles each year).[19]

The first priority for urban policy is to ensure that any new incinerators conform to benchmark emission standards and that existing incinerators are subject to regular environmental assessment.

Waste diversion offers a cheaper alternative. Source separation of waste allows hazardous materials to be identified and dealt with. Waste materials suitable for incineration (such as recycled paper residues) can be handled in specialist incinerators attached to recycled paper mills, where emission controls can be tighter and less hazardous because of the single source of material (and where heat recovery can substitute for bought-in energy). Materials that generate toxic emissions through incineration can be screened out and disposed of more safely.

Reduced traffic

In London, there are an estimated 1.6 million waste-related heavy vehicle movements a year: compactor collection vehicles, skips, waste trucks, lorries carrying rubble, lorries with garden cuttings and tree branches. Waste makes up 6 per cent of the capital's total freight movements. In addition, there are freight deliveries of new materials that could be reduced by recycling, especially of aggregates like sand and gravel (in London they amount to 1.5 million vehicle movements a year). Several policies can reduce road traffic as part of a recycling programme:

- further on-site recycling of construction and demolition waste
- local composting of organic waste from food shops, restaurants and parks
- kerbside pick-ups of bulky household waste instead of individual journeys to CA sites (car journeys to and from CA sites account for 0.7 per cent of all London car journeys)
- establishing small processing plants for the re-manufacture of materials
- removing waste traffic from roads by shifting collection to the pavement (with PCVs)
- designing recycling facilities around water and rail access.

As the Haringey recycling project shows, it is possible to design recycling systems which significantly reduced 'waste miles'.[20]

High-rise estates
One of the main problems of declining conditions on high-rise estates is the breakdown in the management of their waste. Many tower blocks rely on rubbish chutes, but these are no longer adequate for modern waste, particularly cardboard boxes. Chutes get blocked, and waste then finds its way into public areas or is thrown out of windows. On some London estates, we found that chutes were blocked up to half the time. One borough had a special chute unblocking unit whose cost exceeded that of all other waste disposal in the borough. Estate cleaners in another borough were spending up to two-thirds of their time dealing with the problems of waste: collecting it, clearing it up, and cleaning up after it. Where low-rise waste collection generally costs in the region of £20 to £30 a tonne, we found that high-rise waste management costs ten times that amount, most of it falling on the housing account.

A number of boroughs have successfully introduced door-to-door collection of recyclables on estates and reduced costs as a result.[21] Caretakers or cleaners collect boxes of recyclables weekly, and this could be extended to other materials and residual waste as in some private high-rise blocks.

Litter

Street cleaners clear up nearly half a million tonnes of waste each year. In cities, the waste builds up round litter bins and the rubbish put out by shops and restaurants. Much of it is packaging: sweet papers, crisp packets, drinks cans and bottles. Littering has proved remarkably impervious to propaganda campaigns and penalties. The increased cost of waste disposal since the landfill tax has, if anything, made the problem worse by encouraging fly-tipping. A recycling programme – open to traders as well as households, to street markets and venues as well as offices – provides another outlet for some of this litter and also a change in culture. Unsurprisingly, there is a direct correlation between clean cities and those with high-profile recycling programmes (for example Seattle, Toronto and Bath).

Just as recycling works backwards through the systems of industrial production, prompting waste minimisation and redesign, so it can have the same impact in cities. Alongside accessible recycling services, waste-free cities would incorporate recycling into their designs of kitchens and houses, stations and buses. Street litter bins would have compartments as in Germany, and parks would run their own composters.

Rural sustainability

Recycling also addresses key environmental issues in the countryside. Rural areas have traditionally played a twin role in the wider materials economy: supplying both minerals and spaces for landfills. Many counties have produced joint minerals and waste plans, the waste being seen as part of land reclamation.

The new materials regime can help redefine this role. On the one hand, there is a move to restrict quarrying by promoting recycling by the construction industry. On the other, the possibility of ending mixed waste landfill will remove facilities that are now recognised as potentially hazardous: a threat to water courses, to agriculture and to the surrounding population.

Rural areas therefore have a particular interest in the early implementation of the EU's landfill directive and in removing hazards from

A Millennium Product: the Haringey Pedestrian Controlled Vehicle (PCV)

Inspired by a milk float crossed with a street sweeper's cart, the PCV is designed for narrow street pavements. Its operator sorts out recyclables left by householders into builder's bags tied on to the truck, which are then left on the kerbside for a roving collection vehicle to take away for dispatch to recycling factories. The PCV can carry a tonne in weight and costs one-tenth of a large recycling vehicle. It costs only 20p a day to run and its annual running and main-tenance costs are £300. Because it goes on the pavement if requires only one operator.

Everyday, the operator picks up on average 1.75 tonnes of recyclable mate-rials, which will generate a minimum value of £700 once they have been processed in the down-stream economy. If this were incinerated it would lead to sales of electricity of £26, scrap bi-products worth £2 and incur collection and disposal charges of £80.

residual waste. They also have an interest in not replacing landfills with rural mixed waste incinerators. One of the recent waste scares in France arose from the discovery of dioxins in milk produced on farms near a municipal incinerator. Building larger incinerator stacks to spread emissions over wider areas does not address the problem of substances which build up in fatty tissue once they enter the food chain. As in Japan, and most recently in Belgium, waste scares and food scares are beginning to merge.

Instead of being a sink for urban waste, the countryside can use recycled materials to improve its environment. Inert waste (such as rubble and glass) can be used productively as a filler for site reclamation. Organic waste as compost is now in high demand as top soil for land reclamation, as a soil improver and as a growing medium.[22]

Conclusion

Environmental imperatives have been the principal drivers of change in the economy of waste. But while they are reflected in UK central and local government policies towards the environment, they have too often remained unconnected to waste policy, and the environmental benefits of recycling have been underplayed.

These benefits are the central rationale for a new economy of waste. They should shape the character of the emerging regulatory structure, so that environmental objectives become the pole around which the economy re-adjusts itself and its methods of production.

4. 50,000 jobs

In the 1950s the Japanese faced severe raw material shortages. Their producers looked for ways to cut down the materials used in production. They did so by reducing stocks, wastage rates and re-works. To do this they had to re-orient whole chains of production, so that goods were 'pulled through' in response to orders, rather than 'pushed through' to keep production lines going. When a defect occurred they looked for its origin so that it would not happen again. Defects were treated as symptoms, to be traced to their source. The result became known as the 'just in time' system. It could equally be called 'just enough', since its early trigger was material and waste minimisation. In following this idea through, Japanese manufacturers created a new model of mass production which has spread all over the world.

The impact of this kind of change cannot be properly traced in a static calculation of jobs. It has macro effects in raising productivity, profitability and the rate of long-run accumulation, which in turn generate both job destruction and job generation. It is what Schumpeter described as 'creative destruction' and it lies at the heart of long-term growth.

There are signs that the current phase of waste minimisation may have even more radical effects than Japanese manufacturing. We cannot now tell how far it will reach, only recognise its potential. The so-called 'Factor Four' movement is generating technical innovations that produce a fourfold increase in material productivity. Many of the innovations are micro-technologies: new forms of housing and office building; super refrigerators; durable furniture; a quadrupling of existing railway capacity; hypercars weighing only a third of a traditional car and using one tenth of the fuel. But the principles are also being applied to whole sectors, such as energy production and urban transport. In each of these cases, reducing energy and materials and minimising waste are central to process of innovation.

These ideas of minimising resource use are now being reflected in long-term planning in Europe. The recent Austrian National Environment Plan and the Swedish Eco-cycle Commission aim to increase materials efficiency tenfold during the first half of the next century. The Dutch National Environment Plan aims to halve resource use while doubling wealth, and the German Environment Ministry is working on similar targets for reducing materials use, as is the OECD.

Waste minimisation does not end with recycling but it often starts from there. In this chapter, I focus on recycling not only because it is readily realisable but also because it provides a foundation for this wider change. In doing so it acts as a motor of new process technologies and new products. As we can see from those countries that are already well down the recycling road, this in turn leads to exportable technologies and exportable systems.

This chapter focuses on the economic and job creating potential of recycling as the basis for wider change in related environmental industries and systems. In Germany, the waste and recycling sector is bigger than either steel or telecommunications. We estimate that an intensive programme of recycling in the UK could create between 40,000 and 55,000 new jobs, taking into account those that would be lost in the process.

The opportunities are immediately clear to anyone stepping into the sector. During our work in London we started out by interviewing firms involved in re-processing in the UK, in North America and on the continent. At the time (1996–97) those we spoke to in Britain all said that the constraint on their growth was the supply of recycled materials. For most of them increases in these materials would not displace domestic primary materials but imported ones. This sector – even in an era of free trade – provides immediate scope for import substitution.

Material self-reliance and import reduction
Waste is a sector that discourages trade. The principle is that each country, indeed each locality, should be responsible for its own waste.

The Green proximity principle suggests that waste and recycled materials should be treated as close to source as possible, encouraging local production and minimising transport costs.

Unlike waste, there are few restrictions on trade in recyclables. But recycling does not need restrictions, since it develops under the protection of distance. Because it takes place close to the point of consumption, it benefits from the economies of proximity, and can sell its output back into the local market. The greater the transport cost relative to the value of the product, the more local is the 'closed loop'.

This is the first reason why recycling opens up such striking opportunities. Britain has traditionally been an importer of raw materials. The secondary materials economy means that it now has its own stock of resources. Its waste paper is the equivalent of an urban forest. Its metals comprise, as the name used by the Yorkshire-based recycling group indicates, 'urban mines'. In material after material, the balance of production is shifting from the international sources of primary production to the sites of recovery and re-processing.

One example is aluminium. A decade ago, Alcan saw a rise in demand for aluminium drinks cans in Europe. They had to decide whether to invest in a raw material smelter processing bauxite from its global sources or in a plant to recycle cans instead. They decided on the latter and chose Warrington rather than Italy to serve the European market. Given the low level of recovery in the UK, they have had to import the bulk of their used cans but, as UK recycling increases, UK cans substitute for imports.

Other examples include re-treading tyres, electronics recycling and re-usable packaging. In each case, an increase in the productivity of imported materials reduces the need for replacement imports. This is one reason why many of the countries with the highest recycling in Europe are those which historically have had limited access to privileged sources of raw material: Germany, Switzerland, Austria, Denmark and Holland.

If material can be recovered and re-processed more cheaply than primary production, a chain of new economic activity is opened up. The cost of collection and sorting is crucial to this calculation. As we have seen, collecting materials from scattered sources, especially households and small businesses, has always been difficult and expensive. However, six factors are making such collection easier and cheaper:

- the cost of waste disposal has been increasing
- new techniques of collection and sorting are being introduced
- the long-term costs of raw materials are rising, particularly those subject to environmental constraints
- industrial techniques are replacing artisan methods of disassembly and re-processing
- products are now being designed to ease disassembly
- new taxes and charges are being introduced to fund the shortfall, and as they take effect this stimulates innovation and drives down costs

Together they have opened up a new potential field of economic activity.

Re-industrialisation

One starting point for re-industrialisation is the amount of material in the household dustbin. Figure 9 (on pages 52–53) provides our estimates for the UK.[23] Out of the 20 million tonnes of so-called dustbin waste, the largest proportion is 9 million tonnes of putrescible organic waste, with another 8.3 million tonnes of immediately recyclable material. Each of these materials is a resource.

Aluminium
There are some 54,000 tonnes of aluminium cans in the household waste stream, of which two-thirds are landfilled. With our current waste system, we are paying some £2 million to dispose of this material, which would be worth £23 million if delivered baled to an Alcan regional centre and would save a corresponding amount of imports.

Paper
There are an estimated 4.6 million tonnes of paper, of which 2.9 million tonnes is old newspaper and 'printed advertising materials' (PAMs). The long-term pressure on primary forests and the forecast increase in recycled paper production has led to a near doubling of

recycled paper production in Europe from 14 million tonnes in 1983 to 26 million tonnes in 1993 and an expected rise to 42 million tonnes by 2005.

Britain has shared in this growth, and the paper industry provides a model of re-industrialisation. In the early 1980s the UK paper industry was declining, with many mill closures. By 1986 UK production had fallen to 3.9 million tonnes, less than half the national paper consumption. Then things changed. By 1998, production had increased by two-thirds to 6.5 million tonnes and exports had more than trebled.

The reason for this growth is recycling. Paper and card made with recycled inputs reached 4.7 million tonnes in 1998, more than the total industry output a decade earlier. The Aylesford newsprint mill uses 100 per cent recycled paper. The other two UK newsprint mills, in the north west, have both been expanding their recycled content. In May 1999, the Shotton mill on Deeside opened a £34 million extension of its de-inking plant, raising its proportion of recycled input to two-thirds. Tissue mills based on recycled inputs have opened in northern England and Scotland. Seventy-two per cent of UK paper production now uses recycled inputs.

But the recovery is only half complete. Figure 10 (on page 54) shows the sources of used paper that the paper industry regards as readily recoverable. It shows that the UK has 3.5 million tonnes available, the largest source of untapped waste paper in Europe. The cost of disposal is £175 million each year. If it was recycled it would produce paper products worth £2.2 billion, the great majority of which would replace imports.

The challenge for the paper industry is how to access these 'reserves'. The main new sources are offices, public places (like airports or trade fairs) and domestic households. These are the principal 'urban forests' of the next decade.

One example of the 'waste of waste' is office paper in London. Each year Westminster Council sends 130,000 tonnes of high-quality paper by lorry across London to be burnt in the SELCHP incinerator. The Corporation of London sends a further 40,000 tonnes of office paper by barge to be landfilled in Essex. The great bulk of this could be recycled. Office recycling can reach recovery rates of 60 to 70 per cent within a few months, and pays back its investment within eighteen months.[24]

Figure 9. United Kingdom estimated household waste composition

Total households	24,600,000		
Kerbside households	22,140,000		
Estates	2,460,000		

Main recyclables	%	kg/hld/yr	tonnes
news + PAMs	14.4%	119	2,922,480
household paper	3.4%	28	681,912
card packaging	3.4%	28	681,912
corrugated cardbd	1.4%	12	292,248
subtotal paper	*22.6%*	*186*	*4,578,552*
clear glass	4.2%	35	852,390
green glass	3.0%	25	608,850
brown glass	1.1%	8.9	219,186
subtotal glass	*8.3%*	*68*	*1,680,426*
steel cans	2.2%	18	438,372
aluminium cans	0.3%	2.2	53,579
aluminium foil	0.3%	2.5	62,103
aerosols	0.3%	2.5	60,885
subtotal cans etc.	*3.0%*	*25*	*614,939*
HDPE plastic	1.0%	8.4	207,009
PS plastic	0.4%	3.2	77,933
PET plastic	0.8%	6.9	170,478
PP plastic	0.3%	2.5	60,885
PVC plastic	0.1%	1.2	29,225
sacks & carrier bags	1.8%	15	365,310
subtotal plastics	*4.5%*	*37*	*910,840*
textiles/shoes	2.4%	20	487,080
Total main recyclables	**40.9%**	**336**	**8,271,836**

Other refuse			
other metals	0.4%	3.0	73,062
engine oil	0.1%	1.0	24,354
good jumble sale items	0.8%	6.9	170,478
clean wood items	0.3%	2.5	60,885
household batteries	0.1%	1.0	24,354
renovation waste	3.0%	24.8	608,850
plastic film	1.6%	12.9	316,602
other dense plastic	0.8%	6.4	158,301
nappies + other san.	3.6%	29.7	730,620

Other refuse (cont'd)	%	kg/hld/yr	tonnes
other glass	0.3%	2.5	60,885
non-recyclable/compostable paper	0.4%	3.0	73,062
multi-layer pkg	0.8%	6.9	170,478
drink boxes	0.4%	3.0	73,062
miscellaneous other	1.8%	14.9	365,310
fines	0.5%	4.0	97,416
Total other refuse	**14.9%**	**122**	**3,007,719**
Putrescibles			
Central compost			
compostable paper (NR)	2.4%	20	487,080
animal waste	2.4%	20	487,080
meat. bones, etc.	3.4%	28	681,912
subtotal central compost	*8.2%*	*67*	*1,656,072*
Home compost			
compostable kitchen	18.0%	149	3,653,100
garden waste	18.0%	149	3,653,100
subtotal home compost	*36.1%*	*297*	*7,306,200*
Total organic waste	**44.3%**	**364**	**8,962,272**
Total household waste	**100.0%**	**823**	**20,241,827**

Summary	tonnes	%
Recyclable	8,271,836	41%
Putrescible	8,962,272	44%
Other Refuse	3,007,719	15%
Total	**20,241,827**	**100%**
Residential	20,241,827	73%
CA Site	5,400,000	19%
CA Site Diversion	798,000	3%
Street Sweepings	450,000	2%
Special/Manned	600,000	2%
Other Waste	300,000	1%
Domestic Waste	**27,789,827**	**100%**

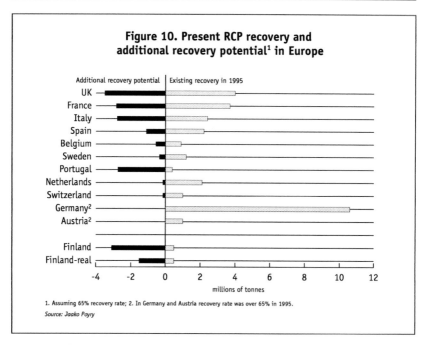

Figure 10. Present RCP recovery and additional recovery potential[1] in Europe

Additional recovery potential | Existing recovery in 1995

UK
France
Italy
Spain
Belgium
Sweden
Portugal
Netherlands
Switzerland
Germany[2]
Austria[2]

Finland
Finland-real

-4   -2   0   2   4   6   8   10   12
millions of tonnes

1. Assuming 65% recovery rate; 2. In Germany and Austria recovery rate was over 65% in 1995.
Source: Jaako Poyry

We estimate (Figure 11) that 3.3 million tonnes of paper could be recovered from domestic bins with intensive recycling schemes, of which 64 per cent are old newspapers and printed advertising materials. Paradoxically, the UK's heavy consumption of newsprint has become a major national resource.

Figure 12 (on page 56) shows that the value of waste paper taken to the Aylesford mill alone is four times the value of all electricity produced by Britain's municipal incinerators, and the waste paper is still a modest fraction of the value added to which it gives rise. Aylesford's sales in 1996 were £150 million, of which a third were exports. The value of all paper production using recycled input in the UK was nearly £2.2 billion, 75 times the value of electricity produced by the incinerator industry.

If the industry is to expand in line with the required growth in recycled paper, then it needs a substantial increase in processing capacity. For the 2.1 million tonnes of news and PAMs alone, five new Aylesford sized plants will be required. Government and industry must give a clear lead to ensure that the growth in European market demand for

Figure 11. United Kingdom household recycling diversion rates (tonnes)

Full Kerbside

household type	kerbside	estates	
household units	22,140,000	2,460,000	
capture rate	75%	50%	total
news + PAMs	1,992,600	132,840	2,125,440
household paper	464,940	30,996	495,936
card packaging	464,940	30,996	495,936
corrugated cardbd	199,260	13,284	212,544
subtotal paper	*3,121,740*	*208,116*	*3,329,856*
clear glass	581,175	30,996	612,171
green glass	415,125	22,140	437,265
brown glass	149,445	7,970	157,415
subtotal glass	*1,145,745*	*61,106*	*1,206,851*
steel cans	298,890	19,926	318,816
aluminium cans	36,531	2,435	38,966
aluminium foil	42,343	2,823	45,166
aerosols	41,513	2,768	44,280
subtotal cans etc.	*419,276*	*27,952*	*447,228*
HDPE plastic	141,143	9,410	150,552
PS plastic	53,136	3,542	56,678
PET plastic	116,235	7,749	123,984
PP plastic	41,513	2,768	44,280
PVC plastic	19,926	1,328	21,254
sacks & carrier bags	249,075	16,605	265,680
subtotal plastics	*621,027*	*41,402*	*662,429*
textiles/shoes	332,100	22,140	354,240
Total main recyclables	**5,598,376**	**357,948**	**5,956,324**

Diversion

	System 1	System 2	System 3
Organic	4,216,535	6,260,700	7,437,662
Recycling	5,956,324	5,956,324	5,956,324
Total Diversion	10,172,859	12,217,024	13,393,987
Percent Diversion	50%	60%	66%

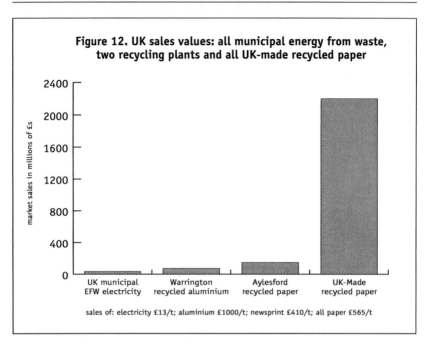

Figure 12. UK sales values: all municipal energy from waste, two recycling plants and all UK-made recycled paper

sales of: electricity £13/t; aluminium £1000/t; newsprint £410/t; all paper £565/t

clear lead to ensure that the growth in European market demand for recycled newsprint is supplied from UK mills.

The recycled paper industry also has significant job-creating potential. Incinerator capacity to dispose of 2.1 million tonnes of newsprint would employ some 250 people. If the paper was used as recycled feedstock in five Aylesford sized mills, it would generate 1,675 direct jobs.

Currently the paper industry as a whole employs 22,000 people, 68 per cent in process and maintenance and 32 per cent as white collar staff. If the industry were to expand to the level of recycling reached in Germany, the number of direct jobs would increase by 11,000 people.

In addition to these 11,000 core jobs. there are jobs created both upstream and downstream in an industry which is replacing imports. One study of the size of such 'indirect' jobs generated by an Aylesford-type mill was made by Professor Pearce of University College in 1995. He estimated that 510 related jobs would be created in commerce and distribution, services and transport, and a further 614 jobs in the investment sector, giving a total of 1,424.[25] A further 2,800 jobs would come through the income multiplier.

Overall, he estimated that each 1,000 tonnes of newsprint capacity leads to 2.7 jobs in value added, 2.0 in investment and 9.2 in the industries stimulated by value added and investment. This means that if one job is created in the mill itself for every 1,000 tonnes of output capacity, each direct mill job should be multiplied by fourteen to judge the potential impact. Given that 2.1 million tonnes of used newspapers would be converted into 1.7 million tonnes of finished newsprint, this would mean that five Aylesford-sized newsprint mills would generate 24,000 jobs.

Not all these jobs would be local – the multiplier includes a significant import component. But, given how much this sector depends on local material sources, it is striking how substantial the domestic employment effect necessarily remains.

The Pearce study also estimates the positive balance of payments effects of a new recycled newsprint mill at £216 per tonne of newsprint recycled. For the 2.1 million tonnes of used newspapers in Table 2 this amounts to £453 million at 1995 prices.[26]

Textiles
A third valuable product in the household waste stream is clothing. Although only constituting 2.4 per cent of the contents of domestic dustbins (some 0.5 million tonnes a year) recycled clothing has a price range of between £100 and £300 a tonne and, like paper, provides an immediate source of import substitution. There is also an established cloth recycling industry – the shoddy manufacturers that developed in the woollen districts of the North. Fibre has been used for stuffing mattresses, for industrial wipers, for felt-making, for carpet underlays and so on. But there is also a strong market for 'nearly new' and second-hand clothing exports (now amounting to 50 per cent of European sorted textiles) and for secondary fibre as an input for reconstituted cloth.

The high value of these products covers the cost of collection and sorting. Sorting conveyor belts separate textiles into as many as 140 categories. Currently only 15 per cent (75,000 tonnes) of domestic textiles are recycled. We estimate that up to 350,000 tonnes are readily recoverable. Currently the 45 principal textile recyclers employ 1,200 people. Expanding the textile recovery industry in line with the expansion of material would generate a further 4,600 new jobs.

Other materials
There are a number of other areas of growth.

Steel cans. There are currently two de-tinning plants, in the north east and south Wales. To process the 319,000 tonnes identified in Figure 11 would require fourteen more such plants distributed throughout the regions, each employing twenty direct operatives.

Plastics. This is the most expensive of the common household materials to collect and transport (because of its lightness). For this reason, where it can be made economic, it is also a good generator of employment. If, as suggested in Figure 11, 660,000 tonnes of plastic are recovered (out of total UK plastic consumption of 4.5 million tonnes) they would need 30 to 50 plants for flaking, pelletising and compounding, which would generate further re-processing of products using recycled plastic.

Glass. Increased recycling of glass would largely substitute for domestic inputs in the glass industry, but there is also scope for expanding production facilities that have developed new uses for glass. Uses include the blasting abrasive, concrete paving, filtration for pools and septic tanks, abrasive wheel manufacture, textured wall coatings and a range of building materials.

Organics. This is the largest domestic stream of all and particularly important given the need to remove it from landfill. On the basis of detailed plans undertaken in Essex, we estimate that extracting and composting organics from the municipal waste stream alone would divert 7.4 million tonnes in the UK and generate at least 7,000 jobs.

These are the main items from the household dustbin. Other products – including white goods (such as fridges and cookers), electric appliances, electronics and car-related waste, together with the construction, or rather the deconstruction, sector – provide similar opportunities. In the UK, 400,000 tonnes of tyres are discarded each year. Increased re-treading or recycling would create 350 to 500 net new jobs in processing alone. Nearly a million tonnes of waste wood is recycled annually and this is set to triple over the next decade, providing inputs for chipboard manufacture. The construction industry recycles 10 million tonnes of hardcore a year out of an estimated 70 million tonnes of construction and demolition (C&D) waste. An increase of C&D recycling to the Danish level of 90 per cent would be a major creator of jobs.

A Danish study of recycling employment estimated that recycling durable products and building waste increased the employment created by recycling in the domestic sector by two-thirds.[27] The German experience confirms this. If the direct expansion of manufacturing and processing employment in 'dustbin materials' as outlined above is minimally 25,000 jobs, then we would expect this to rise to at least 40,000 through intensive recycling in the durable goods, and in waste from the industrial, commercial and construction sectors.

In all of these materials, the gap between the cost of new materials and the cost of recyclables has led producers to choose primary over secondary materials. But as primary materials costs rise and innovations in the secondary materials economy continue, the gap is rapidly closing.

In each case, as recycling becomes feasible and economic, the potential domestic economic gains are substantial. As Figure 12 shows, they dwarf any value salvaged from traditional means of disposal. For the UK, at least, recycling has a high measure of import replacement and, in cases such as paper and textiles, has a significant export component. The new technology involved is also exportable, as the Germans and Scandinavians have demonstrated.

Collection
The economic impact does not stop here, however. As we saw in the case of newsprint, most of the immediate employment impact is on jobs in associated services and investment. Central to these is collection. Collection and all its related aspects are the new frontline of the secondary material economy.

The collectors are secondary lumberjacks, miners and quarry workers rolled into one. As recycling moves into the 'seams' of household and small scale-office and trade waste, a new weight falls on the collection process. As innovation lowers costs and improves yields, collection systems provide the basis for the rapid development of intensive recycling.

Collection is itself a sector, subject to its own economies of scale, scope and density. It is also a major potential generator of jobs. Figure 13 summarises the job impact of a number of different forms of recycling collection.

The highest impact of 50 jobs per 10,000 tonnes collected is made by collection systems using multi-compartment vehicles. These are modifications of the traditional dustcart, with high capital costs and high labour intensity. The medium-cost flatback truck is a standard vehicle. It has wire containers for sorting various recyclable materials. Electric carts, which have the lowest capital costs, employ the fewest number of collectors (32 per 10,000 tonnes) because of their higher labour

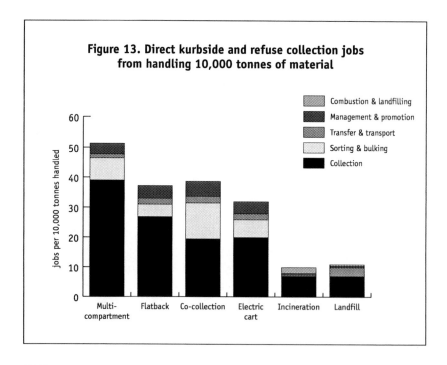

Figure 13. Direct kurbside and refuse collection jobs from handling 10,000 tonnes of material

productivity. This makes collection cheaper, but even then the carts employ three times the number of those working in conventional land-fill and incineration.

As the recycling systems became established, there would be a loss of jobs in disposal, but new recycling collection jobs would more than outweigh them and result in a net employment gain. We would expect a town of 200,000 to generate 122 permanent net collecting, primary sorting and bulking jobs in the long term from the intensive recycling. For the UK this equates to some 15,000 jobs.

From the viewpoint of a municipal waste manager, recycling collection is an expensive supplement to mainstream waste collection. It is expensive because it takes more time to collect and sort recyclables than to handle mass waste and, as an incremental, low volume system, it has high unit costs. But recycling is a declining cost industry. As its yields improve, its costs fall and the income from recovered materials rises. It ceases to be an addition to the main waste collection service and begins to replace it. From the viewpoint of the national economy, the significance goes further. An efficient national system of door-to-door household collection provides a flow of materials for large-scale re-industrialisation.

Conclusion: jobs created and lost

This chapter has concentrated on materials in the domestic dustbin because dustbin waste together with small firm and institutional waste are frontiers for recycling. The evidence from recycling in the UK and overseas shows indisputably that these sectors are potentially a major source of job creation. An intensive recycling programme in Britain provides the scope for 15,000 jobs in collection and sorting and at least 25,000 to 40,000 jobs in manufacturing and re-processing: 40,000 to 55,000 jobs overall.

Recycling will be a net job creator if it satisfies any of three conditions:

● it replaces material imports and/or expands exports
● its labour-intensive components permit it to replace imported capital equipment

● it reduces the costs of material use and disposal, which if reflected in increased profitability and investment, stimulate the rate of growth and employment.

The first two are evident in the main sectors we have discussed. The third is more complex. Financial costs should first be adjusted to reflect the external costs of material use and disposal. Recycling works to lower those costs, and in the longer term it can act to dramatically reduce both financial and environmental costs through innovations that improve the productivity of materials.

This wider impetus has fuelled intensive recycling overseas, nowhere more so than in Germany. A recent study by Dresdner, Kleinwort, Benson of the recycling sector in Germany found that the national waste and recycling industry had more than 1,000 firms, employing an average of 150 people each, with a turnover of between 80 and 100 million DM. Of the 150,000 jobs, 17,000 have been created through packaging recycling alone. This industry is a creation of the 1990s, driven by the environmental movement on the one hand and by government policy on the other. It demonstrates the potential of a sector that is still in the early stages of transformation.

5. Relocalising production

The UK Government has recently established a network of regional development agencies as the flagships of regional economic policy. They are the culmination of nearly two decades of experimentation in local economic development policy and a recognition of the contribution that strong, networked regional economies make to national economic performance.

All such initiatives to promote regional economic development have faced two contrary options. On the one hand, they can compete for mobile national and international investment, providing cheap sites, good communications, generous grants and so on. On the other, they can try to develop home grown activity and support the expansion of small and medium-size enterprises already centred in the region.

The problem with the first option is that it is intensely competitive and that those companies who have the mobility to move in to the region can also move out again. The problem with the second is that it may create few net jobs, success for some being at the expense of others. Both alternatives reflect dream images: one a vision of the self-regulating global market economy, the other a self reliant local economy.

The tension between the two has a direct bearing on the secondary materials economy. One criticism levelled at community-based recycling networks is that they are unsustainable in the face of globalisation: their small-scale operations are no match for the power of mechanisation, internationalisation and global corporations. But the evidence suggests that the possibilities are more complex than this. The development of the waste economy shows that the local and the global can be interdependent in productive and sustainable ways. Developing large-scale recycling systems depends on innovation from grassroots organisations. Sustaining them depends on linking such networks to new international markets and on wiring the systems together at local and regional level. When this re-wiring is successful, it creates local economic activity that is efficient and employment that is stable and rooted in local areas. Achieving this requires us to understand three elements of the new system:

- the role of local, community-based networks
- the creation of regional-level processing and re-manufacturing plants that can draw on local materials and use existing infrastructure
- the connections between these producers and wider international markets.

Grassroots beginnings

First, the recycling economy begins with local roots. Collectors go where the rubbish is, which is everywhere, from the smallest village to the highest tower block. The 15,000 collection jobs that could be generated by recycling would be spread relatively evenly throughout the country. They can be promoted by local councils, by parishes or by tenants associations; by chambers of commerce among small traders, by schools and by local sports clubs. As a rough measure, 400 tonnes of recyclables, or approximately 1,640 households (1,100 households if organics are added), will support one full-time job equivalent.

Second, collection thrives on diversity. In developing intensive recycling in Essex, we found that no one model of collection and composting suited each of the eleven authorities. Uttlesford is large and rural, with 54 parishes. Tendering is divided in three by estuaries. Harlow is still a new town, broken into eight neighbourhoods, each with their local committees and municipal budgets. Chelmsford unites town and country and, like Rochford, collects its waste in wheeled bins. The people who knew how to collect more with less were those local officers who had worked the routes for years and the neighbourhoods with their knowledge of spare spaces. Good collection depends on distributed intelligence.

Third, domestic collection depends on the householder to perform a measure of unpaid labour. A successful scheme needs not just consent but an element of commitment. International experience shows that recycling must be easy for the householder if the scheme is to succeed. Householders must have the right equipment (boxes and bins) and advice. Financial incentives (and penalties) are not enough. Community collectors achieve higher yields than local councils, who in turn do better than larger waste firms. Because householders are involved, the principles of the gift economy are combined with exchange: values other than the purely financial are necessary for recycling to work.

This is one reason why community enterprises have been so successful in this field. The Haringey collection system described in chapter three is now being passed over to a local community enterprise. A similar system in Islington is already run by a long-standing community recycling group and is achieving the highest capture rates in London. Kerbside recycling collections in Hounslow, Ealing, Lambeth and Brent are run by Ealing Community Recycling. All these groups are members of the Community Recycling Network (CRN), an association of more than 100 recycling groups. Association members are responsible for the leading recycling collection schemes in Bath and Avon and, taken together, are the largest operators of recycling schemes in the UK.

The role of community enterprise
What role do these groups have in larger-scale systems? One view is that they are little more than multinational sub-contractors, subject to the pressures and vulnerability of globalisation. Large metal and paper companies have often had to get into the collection of waste materials because there was no one else to do it, but their job is manufacturing not doorstep collection. In principle, they are only too pleased if there are small, locally connected collection schemes that can provide reliable flows of recycled inputs. On this view such schemes are tightly constrained by the realities of the global economy.

Another version of this argument is that the community enterprises and similar small, local collection firms are the pioneers of a sector that is not fully formed. They are willing to operate at or below the financial margin because of their commitment to the job. As the sector becomes more established, larger firms will move in and replace the horizontal links of local networks with the vertical structures of a large corporation. There is some evidence of this in North America and Germany.

However, both these reactions miss the true significance of these operations. They are certainly pioneers and innovators, but they also have a longer-term place in the systems that they help to create. Viewed historically, the Green values on which the community enterprises have relied support the small, the light footed and the local. These values fit well with household and neighbourhood services. It is an ideology which privileges diversity and detail, and the free sharing of experience and ideas. But this model also fits the wider contours of the knowledge economy and its productivity is shown by the innovations that it has already produced.

To increase the scale of recycling, however, other support is needed. Vertical organisations like large firms provide economies of scale in activities such as marketing, bulk purchasing, bidding for local government contracts and access to finance, management information systems and technological knowledge. However, it is striking that in the US, where large firms did replace the community sector, they are now shedding recycling because they cannot make it pay. In part, this is because they have found it difficult to handle the decentralised diversity that local recycling entails. The German experience is similar: diseconomies of scale have led to 'heavy' systems and higher costs.

A different response

The Community Recycling Network has shown that it is possible to create alternative solutions to the problems of scale. For example, they have established a material sales consortia. They have set up an advisory consultancy drawn from their members to help new groups and existing operations. They operate an international information and technological search function, whose results are diffused through internal papers, workshops and the Internet. They have designed their own vehicles and developed model contracts and tender proposals for local authorities. An associate group has established a complementary trade and waste composition analysis service. All these have arisen in response to operational requirements. They were not inspired by the models of industrial districts in continental Europe that have attracted such interest in the past decade, or by the works on the organisation of the new knowledge economy. But it is striking how closely they reflect both.

The jobs created by community enterprises are not make-work jobs: rather they are the starting point for the next stage of the secondary materials economy described in the previous chapter. There is a material *raison d'etre* for collection to be organised in this way. They need not necessarily be run by not-for-distributed-profit groups. A similar style of operation could be operated by an innovative municipal direct service organisation, or by a local firm, or by a modern, internally networked corporation.[28] The point is that the most efficient way of performing this part of the recycling loop also provides stable, locally rooted employment. The local and the efficient are, in this case, synonymous.

How far can this spread?

The question for local economic policy is how far this argument can be extended into the 'closed loop' of the recycling economy. One way to answer this is to examine how far community enterprise already extends. There are already a number of parallel networks to the CRN.

A community composting network that promotes local compost projects. Composting is an activity where levels of contamination tend to go with scale. The back garden composter will not contaminate their bin if they know that the compost will be used in the same garden. A similar principle holds for small-scale community composting, whereas contamination is more difficult to control in large-scale facilities with anonymous collection systems.

Consumer durable recycling and re-use schemes. In France, there is a network of 28 community enterprises that re-use and recycle white goods. It is organised on a quasi-franchise basis, with services provided by a central not-for-profit group, similar in structure and culture to the CRN (see box over). In the UK, there are many initiatives of this kind which re-circulate white goods. One of the best developed is Create in Liverpool, which is now expanding in Yorkshire and London. There is a similar network for enterprises reclaiming furniture.

Job training in recycling: experience from France and the UK

The French white goods network Envie has been established to provide training for low qualified, unemployed people, on an intermediate labour market model similar to that of the Wise Group in the UK. Trainees are taken on for an average of fourteen months and a maximum of two years, and provide a white goods reclamation service, whose output is then sold on to those on low wages. Between 1989 and 1993 Envie opened 28 centres in large cities in France and it has a further three due to open shortly. A full 70% of its funding comes from sales revenue on reclaimed equipment, with 30% from national funds, worth about £5,000 per place per year, which are committed on a long-term basis, and topped up to £7,000 from local sources. The network provides 400 trainee jobs per year (paid at the rate of £8,000 per year) with 60% of those completing a training cycle of at least eighteen months going on to find employment. In addition, it has created 100 permanent executive jobs and a further 40 permanent administrators.

In the UK, Create in Liverpool operates on a similar model and provides an annual programme for twenty salaried trainees, 68% of whom go on to permanent jobs. In addition to the trainees jobs, they employ eleven permanent staff. The cost of operations is similar to that of the Wise Group (from £16,000 to £18,000 per place per year), and they currently cover 60% through trading revenue. The hardest task is financing the shortfall, because of the constantly changing nature of UK funding programmes and the different funding conditions in the towns and areas in which they have been working. Their Liverpool project has been funded under the Employment Zone scheme which is coming to an end for that area, and they hope now to move to New Deal finance. What is needed for the model to spread is a national scheme of long-term intermediate labour market funding which would then allow districts to establish the white good reclamation service on the Envie model.

The environmental potential of these schemes can be judged by the fact that 5 to 6 million appliances are discarded each year in the UK, with an estimated weight of 350,000 tonnes, or 1% of the annual municipal waste stream. In the past, 80% of these were recycled, mainly through shredding often in conjunction with cars. Since the introduction of the landfill tax, increasing numbers of appliances have been diverted from trade pick ups into the municipal waste stream, many of which go straight to landfills. Envie estimates that after reconditioning 25% of domestic appliances are suitable for domestic use, and this further reduces energy and materials use relative to recycling. Overall, the Envie network collects and examines 250,000 appliances per year, (5% of the French total) of which 60,000 are repaired, and the remainder sent to recycling.

A network to recycle computers. The concerns involved are intermediaries, taking computers being replaced by large companies, clearing their memory, repairing and updating them and passing them on to the voluntary sector, usually with a training package.

Terry towel nappy laundry services. Organised by the Real Nappy Association, which provides collection, laundry and delivery, this scheme has been notably successful in Milton Keynes.

Charcoal burning. This is a network of 50 small enterprises producing charcoal from waste wood and selling it through local B&Q outlets. The network is organised on a quasi-franchise basis, where the central service group negotiates the outlets, identifies suitable burning equipment, and provides training.

These networks have a number of common features. Their driving force is social and environmental commitment rather than financial returns. The enterprises are subject to commercial discipline but their goal is to expand impact/output subject to financial sustainability. In many cases, their not-for-distributed-profit status is central to their operation. The computers, white goods and furniture are passed on partly in the knowledge that they will be recirculated in the social economy. Some have been established specifically to provide work or training. Most are small scale and operate on an artisan basis.

In some cases, for example composting and charcoal, this is the appropriate scale. Consumer durable and computer recycling are likely at some point to be subject to industrialised disassembly and repair. It may be possible for networks like those in France to develop this scale of operation and to maintain a specialisation in the social economy. Or they could develop a specialism in collection and initial screening before dispatch to specialised disassembly facilities. However, all of the examples illustrate the scope for a continued role in local collection and delivery, however large scale the recycling of a particular material stream might become.

Processing and re-manufacturing

While collection is necessarily local, it is not so clear that re-processing and manufacturing plants for secondary materials can be connected to local economies in the same way. If these industries are becoming global, how can they remain rooted in regions? Again, experience from the UK and North America shows that regional systems can be highly effective.

One striking is example is Temple Cloud in north-east Somerset. A community enterprise collects recyclables from villages using two Persheron horses and a cart with cages. From there the newspaper goes to Aylesford in Kent, the aluminium to Alcan in Warrington, the steel cans to British Steel in south Wales and the glass to Rockware in Yorkshire. These are all international firms, geared to national and European markets.

There is also a potential space for local and regional manufacturing. The best example is paper. There is still scope for import substitution in tissue, and of the twelve tissue mills in the UK, four have capacities of between 12,000 and 33,000 tonnes and the largest two are just over 100,000 tonnes each, well within the scope of a regional market to supply. In office paper, which still has a low level of recycled input, two-thirds of UK mills have a capacity of 50,000 tonnes or less per year, a size which would allow the Borough of Westminster alone to support two recycled mills.

One of the most innovative environmental groups in the UK, the Bio-Regional Development Group in Sutton, Surrey, has gone a step further, They have developed a project to make office paper for the regional market from a mixture of locally collected recycled paper and hemp grown in Essex.

Even in newsprint, which requires large-scale production, smaller-scale urban mini-mills have grown in the United States during the 1990s. The cost disadvantages of smaller scale are outweighed by their ability to use existing infrastructure and by lower transport costs. The Finnish paper consultants Jaakko Poyry recently reported that mini-mills would be viable in the UK for newsprint, office paper, white liner board and tissue if they could be located near existing sources of heat and power, good transport links and water sources. This would put even a midi newsprint mill within reach of a region undertaking intensive recycling with a catchment area of 4 million people.[29]

One of the most ambitious schemes of this kind was developed by a community coalition in the Bronx area of New York. The coalition has designed, financed and built a community controlled newsprint mill that will produce 220,000 tonnes of finished newsprint using 25 per cent of New York's waste newspapers. This is the first industrial enterprise to open in the Bronx since 1947. It involves £290 million investment, created 2,200 jobs during its construction phase and 450 permanent direct jobs.[30]

Developing a regional 'recycling loop' depends on smaller-scale processes which can serve a local or regional market. Where it is difficult to organise processes such as glass bottle making at a smaller scale, a regional authority can promote other uses for recycled inputs that can operate at this level. A glass tile plant for example requires 20,000 tonnes of input per year, which is a catchment area of 440,000 households, smaller than many counties. Aluminium cans can be reprocessed in smaller foundries for a range of purposes. Detinning plants for steel cans have a capacity of 20,000 tonnes, requiring a catchment area of 1.5 million households. Currently there are only two such plants in the UK. Intensive recycling in Britain would support fifteen regional plants of this size.

For materials like textiles, compost and plastics, plants can be relatively small and localised. The constraint for open windrow composting is the turning mechanism, which with current technologies operates most economically at a throughput of 8,000 tonnes per annum. This would require a catchment area of 30,000 to 40,000 households. Taking Essex as an example, with some 600,000 households there are currently four compost processing centres, to which the Essex intensive recycling strategy proposes to add a further twelve.

The initial stage of textiles sorting requires a catchment area of 175,000 households, and a plastics re-processing plant something of the same order. Together with compost processing, operations of this size are ideal elements for a local economic development programme.

The implication of this evidence is that, in each region, a ring of processing and re-manufacturing facilities could be developed to serve larger markets and the home regional economy. In the South-west,

Bristol Council is already undertaking research into plastics and organic processing. There is good access to the steel sector in south Wales, and to at least two paper mills.

This sets a challenge for the new regional development agencies: they should work with local collection authorities to build up local processing capacity that matches the expanded supplies of recycled materials, and with the private sector to expand the recycling of wood, construction and demolition waste, tyres and commercial organics. Regional economic policy plays a crucial role in linking the local to the global.

This conclusion is further supported by the success of many North American states in encouraging local recycling loops. The Clean Washington Centre in Seattle is a leading example. It has worked with local firms using virgin materials imported from outside the state to see if they could convert to secondary materials. It has developed new products that can use recycled materials and disseminated information on how it they can be used. Overall it has generated 1,865 jobs in eight years, in a total recycling industry whose workforce has grown from 3,000 to 18,000 in ten years, 14,000 of them in manufacturing.

Recycling development agencies of this kind have been established by a number of US states and have now been replicated in Australia and New Zealand. They show that recycling is a strong stimulus to a more integrated local economy and to local manufacturing jobs. A detailed study of the Tri-City Region of Baltimore, Maryland showed that this kind of programme could, over time, create 6,000 manufacturing jobs and switch the main sources of secondary materials from outside to within the region (see box opposite for US recycling related jobs).

This forecast, if born out, suggests that the argument of chapter four, that recycling in the UK provides a basis for import substitution, also applies at regional level. Because the recovered materials are widely distributed (in contrast to most primary materials), the processing of materials with a low value-to-weight ratio will be encouraged to locate close to the sources of secondary materials (because of transport costs). This tendency towards 'localising' the recycling loop can be reinforced by technical change.

Economic activity and job creation through recycling: experience from the United States

- New Jersey (with a 43% recycling rate) reported having 9,000 jobs in scrap based manufacturing alone (Lewis 1994).
- Maine (42% rate) estimated that as early as 1992 recycling had added 2,000 jobs to the state economy, with 600 employed in scrap based manufacturing, and a further 770 in industries supporting the core producers (O'Hara).
- Pennsylvania (recycling rate 26%) estimated recycling-related jobs in their state at 10,000 (Biocycle 1993).
- A study of ten North Eeastern American states calculated that recycling had added $7.2 billion in value to recovered materials through processing and manufacturing activities. A total of 103,000 people were employed in recycling-related industries in the region in 1991, 25% of them in processing and 75% in manufacturing (paper being the most important) (Weston 1994).
- In Washington state, which recycles 39% of its waste, 16,700 people are employed in recycling related industries, over 14,000 of them in manufacturing, and the remainder in collection and sorting. This is a 39% increase or 4,700 jobs in the six years between 1989 and 1995. In addition, recycling generated $1.5 billion in capital investment, $1.4 billion in the recycled content manufacturing sector, while recycling related construction contributed $1.7 billion to the local economy (Clean Washington Centre estimates, 1997).
- A study in Massachusetts (recycling rate 34%) in 1991 calculated that the state had more than 200 recycling related facilities, which handled 1.75 million tonnes of scrap each year and added nearly $600 million to its value. The majority (178) were involved in processing, and a further 26 in manufacturing based on secondary materials. Manufacturing accounted for half the 9,467 jobs in the sector, with processing providing a further 25% (Lewis 1994).
- Minnesota (recycling rate 45%) estimated that 90 recycling-based manufacturers employed 8,700 people directly, and generated a further 9,300-17,300 jobs in indirect and induced activities. Direct sales were $1.5 billion, and state tax revenue between $40 million and $66 million (Minnesota OEA 1997).
- A study by the Institute of Local Self Reliance (Morris and Seldman 1993) of Baltimore, Washington DC and Richmond, a region with recycling rates of 23% to 30%, found that: 5,100 people are employed in recycling related enterprises as against 1,100 in waste disposal, even though waste disposal handles three times as much material; a tonne of recovered material generates $120 (£78) in revenue; and a tonne of recovered material manufactured into an end product generates $1,140 (£745) in revenue.

See end of notes for sources

Urban and rural policy

The analysis outlined here has important implications for urban regeneration policy. Throughout the industrial world, cities have faced a flight of manufacturing jobs over the past 25 years. Recycling provides a rationale for a reversal of the trend. The principle of the urban mini paper mills has a more general application. If waste and final markets are concentrated in the cities, then there is a cost factor that encourages local re-manufacture, particularly where it can take advantage of existing infrastructure. The fact that markets and consumption are concentrated in cities means that cities are also concentrations of secondary resources.

The Clean Washington Centre has shown the scope for regional development agencies to work with existing firms on replacing imported primary materials with secondary ones, and to create the economic and technical conditions to attract new firms. Another possibility, started in Italy and being explored in the UK and Ireland, is to construct 'eco-industrial complexes' in formerly industrialised urban areas, which would bring together re-processors in a range of sectors.

Recycling also offers to strengthen rural economies. Country districts have traditionally been seen as high cost for collection purposes. But some of the highest recycling rates (over 70 per cent) have been achieved at village level in Kent by intensive recycling and composting: residual waste in these villages is now down to 4 kilograms per household per week.

These villages show that small communities have certain advantages. They can reduce and recycle much of their waste within the parish. Dry recyclables can be stored until there are economic loads or be jointly loaded onto vehicles carrying other goods. There is often a stronger sense of community for such projects and, for parish councils and village shops, recycling provides increased income. A parish of 2,000 households would produce 1,100 tonnes of recyclables and organics a year, yielding an income from sales and saved costs of around £50,000. This is a significant inflow for many rural areas.

Conclusion

Recycling does not pit the local against the global. The two are connected. There are some closed local and regional loops, but other materials soon find their way to international markets. The local is part of the global, and the global system depends on local collection and distribution. It must be able to connect to the many streams and tributaries that feed into larger flows, and this is only possible by drawing on systems that can penetrate right to the heart of local communities.

For development agencies and community economic development initiatives, there are two main areas of action. The first is to promote local and regional loops, the second is to use wider markets to increase the sustainability of local economies. In doing so they can help to strengthen production systems as a whole.

6. Recycling and social policy

Alongside its potential for the environment, the economy and local regeneration, recycling also offers a social dividend. It bears on social policy in three ways:

- increasing environmental equity
- providing new opportunities for 'green collar' jobs and welfare-to-work
- extending productive democracy.

Environmental equity

The distribution of waste and hazards follows social contours, just like the distribution of income. Historically waste was transported from northern countries to the developing world, a practice partially stopped by the Basle ban.[31] Within countries, however, there is no such restriction. A 1995 US Supreme Court ruling that prevents states from blocking the import of waste from other states is currently the subject of a major challenge, argued on the grounds of human rights and environmental justice.

As long as there is mixed waste for disposal and free internal trade in waste, disposal sites, particularly incinerators, will be located in poor urban areas. Incinerators tend to be in old industrial zones, which historically are also low income areas. These areas have less political influence in preventing new sites, and higher income groups are more able to move out of areas where incinerators or landfills are designated.

Friends of the Earth has recently confirmed this view by correlating emissions with income data by postcode. They found that the poorest families (under £5,000 average income per year) were twice as likely to live near a polluting factory as households with incomes over £60,000. The greatest inequalities were in London and the North-east. As we have seen in earlier chapters, the two incinerators servicing the London area and producing toxic emissions as a result are located in Enfield/Tottenham and Lewisham, both deprived areas. Proposals for new incinerators are concentrated in east London.

There are two approaches to improving environmental equity in waste. First, we can reduce the incidence of hazards. Second is to apply the principle of local self-sufficiency in waste disposal, which would restrict any area from off-loading its disposal problems on its neighbours. These approaches complement each other, since any area faced directly with the threat of toxic disposal is more likely to seek non-toxic solutions.

A similar argument applies to litter. Waste managers often remark that litter attracts litter. A litter box or small pile left uncleared will attract more. Fly-tipping feeds on itself. The end of pipe solution depends on the resources for street cleaning and clearance. This is unequally distributed according to income (Westminster spends four and a half times as much on refuse collection and street cleaning as Hackney, despite having a smaller population). Recycling aims to reduce litter in the first place. As with hazard reduction, the emphasis is on prevention.

Waste and work
Distributed employment
Chapters four and five showed how the new recycling economy promises a substantial increase in jobs, which would be more evenly distributed geographically than other alternatives. Much of the associated processing can be targeted to areas where it is most needed. For these reasons, recycling, like energy and water conservation, is an excellent instrument for local job generation programmes.

Recycling does not automatically produce these jobs, but it gives those managing the waste economy, and specifically local authorities, the scope to introduce recycling in ways that meet wider social policy objectives. One of these is the number of local jobs. Another is their quality.

Quality of work

The quality of jobs in recycling varies considerably according to the methods used. One model, common in Germany, is to limit kerbside sorting and separate mixed recyclables in large sorting factories. In the US, and now in the UK, the process goes further because the mixed waste also includes putrescible waste (so-called 'dirty MRFs'). In these cases the collection jobs are similar to those of a traditional dustman, while those on the sorting line are monotonous and hazardous. An unpublished study by the Federal Agency for Workplace Safety in Germany found that waste sorting stations are among the country's most unhealthy workplaces. It noted the impact of bacteria from rotting foodstuffs on air quality, and the frequent small cuts and wounds that workers suffered from the sharp edges of cans.[32]

A collection system based on source separation and kerbside sorting requires a different form of 'green collar' work. Collectors are responsible for frontline quality control of the materials, using information to analyse the performance of the service, and relations with the householder. They also need to develop materials know-how and statistical skills, to organise and analyse information from waste composition studies, participation and capture data, and logistics management. Just as frontline workers have gained a new prominence in a modern manufacturing plant, so recycling collectors become a pivot of the new multi-material collection systems. These people have been the source of many recent innovations.

Recycling collection and advisory services also draw on skills that are widely available in local communities but not necessarily validated in the labour market – social and communication skills, knowledge of a locality and language. Just as hospitals now employ ethnic minorities as an interface between minority communities and the health service, recycling can do likewise. The Haringey scheme was given a great boost when it was taken up and promoted within the borough's Turkish community.

Green skills

The labour intensity of collection and advisory work, and the range of skills required, means that this form of recycling and composting is well suited to the Environmental Task Force and welfare-to-work programmes. It provides the opportunity for participants to develop skills that are demanded by the expansion of recycling. Welfare-to-work recruits would also be a great asset in establishing recycling programmes, which are particularly labour intensive in their early stages.

Local authorities are in a good position to organise programmes of this kind because of their experience with earlier job creation programmes, and some have already provided welfare-to-work places in recycling. To give an idea of the potential scale, a town of 100,000 households with an intensive recycling programme would be able to provide 40 task force placements in collection and sorting, social marketing and householder liaison.

Productive democracy

A third feature of recycling touches on the issue of economic democracy in a more limited way than is normally discussed, but with a wider range. Well-managed recycling schemes are remarkable popular. Polling data regularly shows more than 95 per cent support for recycling, and it is commonly voted the most popular service in municipal polling. This may at first seem strange. Householders are being asked to take more trouble in their handling of waste. They receive no financial compensation for doing so, yet they regularly press to extend it. Why only newspapers? What about writing paper and cardboard? Can no one use the plastics? We have seen recycling schemes which are grossly mismanaged and cavalier in their conduct, yet still residents put out material in support of an idea.

We can explain this popularity as an instance of 'productive democracy'. Recycling offers people a way of doing something about an issue of common concern. Like the growth of Green and ethical consumption, people are finding ways of expressing values through small daily acts, rather than leaving it all to politicians. The emergence of consumers as producers is part of a broader shift towards breaking down the dislocation of political life between the passive citizen and the active government. The tenor of modern government is to find ways for citizens to participate in the production of their services.

There is also scope to take such engagement further. As we saw in chapter five, recycling is well suited for operation by self-managed groups and community enterprises. Some boroughs have discussed proposals for 'community franchising' through which collection rounds can be taken over by community groups, with the support and services provided by a central unit. Collection groups would be able to organise their own working schedule in co-ordination with house-holders and other municipal collectors. This flexibility of working time is often critical for those not in a position to take on full time jobs. Recycling can provide an economic foundation for tenants on council estates or for parish councils.

One of the problems faced by the co-operative movement in the past was that it mirrored traditional corporate organisation. We can speak of Fordist co-ops just as much as Fordist corporations, which reproduce the rigid hierarchical structures found in other sectors. The new model of 'nested' organisations opens up areas of autonomy for people engaged in direct production, but with access to support and a means of integration into wider systems provided by a core management.

The social and the economic

Recycling offers a new way of recombining social and economic objectives. Social policy has historically had an unresolved relationship to the economy. One strain in welfare thinking has been that the economy should be left to itself and public welfare policy should mop up afterwards. Another has been to try to manage the economy so that welfare goals are woven into its workings. The liberal tradition of the early twentieth century took this second view, uneasy with the degree of state control over unemployed people that was implied by Fabian-inspired welfare systems.[33] Social insurance and macroeconomic policy both reflected this approach, but an integration of the social and the economic was also found in the traditions of the co-operative and trade union movements, and in the social democratic argument for public ownership.

Late twentieth century social democracy is exploring new ways to re-combine the social and the economic. One example is the philosophy, resonant of the early twentieth century, that the best form of welfare is work. But the point goes further, to promoting the third sector and co-operatives as a form of collective self-help, and to engaging private companies in the delivery of social objectives. The ethical trading initiative is one example of this wider move to emphasise the social character and responsibility of companies.

If waste management shifts towards recycling by developing an alliance of stakeholders around these diverse goals, then it allows what would normally be classified as external benefits to be realised as part of the re-organisation of a productive system. Doing this in practice requires us to be able to measure social, environmental and other impacts in different ways than through conventional financial cost–benefit analysis. The richness of information that recycling and secondary materials systems embody points to an enhanced capacity for such measurement: through indicators of social capital, community participation, work created among those usually marginalised from the labour market, householder satisfaction, skills development and so on.

The triple dividend

To the double helix of the economy and the environment we can add two further strands: local regeneration and social equity. We can see these as dimensions of waste: as potential dividends. The normal discourse of waste is more restricted. The prime concern of waste managers is waste management. Wider environmental benefits have not determined most disposal strategies, and economic and social benefits have been largely excluded. This is because our systems of government are still not well suited to handling multi-dimensional problems.

The striking opportunities opened up by recycling question the role of government particularly sharply. Until now, the organisation of government and its budget has been arranged around discrete 'line items' and has focused on deciding between separate allocations. Today, the task of government is the connection and management of multiple goals. How can budgets and the wider structures of governance be arranged so that projects and services can deliver these goals and outcomes? The contemporary question is less about how much money is spent and more about *how* it is spent. In a prescient article on the twentieth century need for synthesis over separation, written in 1926, the painter Kandinsky saw it as a movement from an age of 'either/or' to one of 'both/and'.[34] The UK's Social Exclusion Unit was established in this spirit, not to spend money but to see how multiple goals could be achieved. This is the challenge both to national and local government.

Part II. The impasse

'What happens then is the diffusion of a new set of generic technologies, capable of rejuvenating and transforming practically all existing industries, together with the creation of a group of new dynamic industries, at the core of radically new technology systems (paradigms). These are the technological revolutions described by Schumpeter as "creative gales of destruction". They have occurred about every 50 or 60 years and it is this phenomenon that lies at the root of the so-called long waves in economic growth.... During paradigm transitions, there are very intense transformations in technology and the economy and a high level of inertia and confusion in the socio-institutional sphere. It is this difference in rhythm of change that leads to the decoupling which we hold is characteristic of the downswing decades of the Krondatiev long waves. The upswing decades begin as structural coherence is re-established, by means of vast socio-institutional innovations, in response to the requirements of the new paradigm and geared to facilitating the full transformation in the productive sphere ... in (periods of transition) institutions face a chaotic and unaccustomed situation, which requires much deeper changes than the great majority of leaders and members have experienced. The difficulty is increased by the fact that there are no proven recipes and change has to take place by trial and error experimentation under the pressure of the very high social costs of the techno-economic transformation.'

Carlota Perez, *New Technologies and Institutional Change 1996*

7. Perverse markets

Britain has conspicuously failed to take advantage of the economic and social opportunities that recycling offers. While leading European countries and states are recycling 40 per cent or more of their municipal waste, Britain remains stuck at less than 8 per cent. The government's recommendation of 1995, that 25 per cent household waste should be recycling by 2000, looks very unlikely to be achieved.

Britain has also been largely by-passed by the secondary materials revolution. It recycles only 16 per cent of its steel cans (against 80 per cent in Germany), 30 per cent of its glass bottles (89 per cent in Switzerland) and 38 per cent of its paper (compared to 71 per cent in Germany). Despite the largest 'urban forest' in Europe, Britain still imports nearly 60 per cent of its paper (principally made from virgin wood) and a quarter of its pulp. Out of 9 million tonnes of domestic green waste, the Department for the Environment, Transport and the Regions estimates that only 213,000 tonnes (2 per cent) was composted in 1995–96.

Instead of leading the change to recycling, and building an industry behind it, the UK has been a follower. Waste is still treated as waste, rather than as a resource for new industries. Its economic development potential has been strangely inverted, so that the lack of markets for secondary materials is seen as a major weakness of the recycling alternative. What other sector, when faced with a quadrupling of demand, would interpret this as a problem? While there is an issue of supply leading demand, it is an issue of transition. The long-run trend points only one way.

Despite widespread consensus on the desirability of waste minimisation and recycling, the conditions that have led to their expansion overseas have not been created. Changes in taxation, subsidy and regulation have caused further confusion, and the view has grown up that major change is impossible. Instead, the ground has been prepared for a massive growth in incineration. The minister recently told the House of Lords environment sub-committee that 55 to 170 new incinerators may now be needed in the UK.

Even at current rates of emissions control, the costs of an incineration-based strategy threaten a crisis in local government finance. Building the capacity to burn half of forecast municipal waste would require investment of £4 billion. Contracts to manage an incineration-based strategy would cost £54 billion, excluding collection, or some £2 billion each year. This would double current local authority disposal costs and the costs would rise over time.

Given the environmental and financial costs of such a strategy, and the missed opportunities that chapters one to six set out, this seems strange. How can a government committed to environmental, economic and social development find itself in a corner where incineration seems the only way out? The answer is not personal or conspiratorial. It reflects the difficulty of moving from one industrial order to another. These problems are not unique to the waste sector and understanding how they can be overcome points to wider lessons for governance models and economic development strategies in the future.

In this chapter I argue that intensive recycling has been held back in Britain by short term economics: the structure of the waste market prevents longer-term investment in recycling, because the subsidies and incentives on offer do not reflect the full costs of the different waste treatment options, and because the market is distorted by monopoly purchasing power in different sectors. Recycling is seen by many local authorities as an extra cost, an 'add-on' to existing waste services. However, our analysis shows that, over time, intensive recycling programmes actually reduce the cost of waste management, regardless of subsidies. Achieving this requires a long-term view of the *whole system* of waste management and materials supply.

The economics of environmental transition

For those working in the waste sector, recycling has not taken off for economic reasons. No one can afford it. In municipal waste, council budgets are squeezed and markets for recyclables are uncertain. Like libraries, swimming pools and other discretionary services, recycling has to be a low priority when even statutory services are being cut.

For most councils, recycling has remained a marginal service. They have funded cheap forms of recycling like bring banks and low-intensity kerbside collection of paper, which largely pay for themselves. They have begged and borrowed from government grant programmes or taken on private sector sorting equipment. They have benefited from recycling credits paid by the disposal authorities for materials diverted from disposal. But in general, spending on recycling has to be limited by its income. Given that intensive multi-material kerbside collection may cost anything from £90 to £140 a tonne to start, and that material sales income and recycling credits may run from £40 to £70 a tonne, there is a recycling gap. All but a few intrepid councils have failed to bridge this gap.

Recycling does not attract the private sector for the same reason: in itself it is not seen as profitable. Some of the secondary material processors run or finance their own schemes, using low cost (and low recovery) options for single materials like glass or paper. But intensive collection *itself* does not make money: it lies beyond the margins of the market.

In fact, the structure of market incentives in the UK is almost the exact reverse of the environmental policy hierarchy. A recent financial analysis of the waste sector presented hierarchies of price and profitability (see Figure 14 over). It found that the highest prices are for treating hazardous waste, followed by municipal disposal, incineration and landfill. The lowest are inert landfill and recycling. The report notes that

this hierarchy reflects both the licensing barriers to entry and the costs associated with the treatment/disposal undertaken. Notwithstanding political rhetoric and pressure groups, recycling remains a commercial leper in the UK. Prices for recovered materials, in particular, are very depressed. Thus it can often

Figure 14. Waste industry hierarchies

Waste industry environmental policy hierarchy

Reduce

Re-use

Recycle/Compost

Incineration with heat and power

Incineration with power

Incineration without heat or power

Landfill with energy recovery

Landfill

Waste industry price hierarchy

Hazardous waste incineration

Clinical waste

Hazardous landfill

Municipal incineration

Municipal landfill

Liquids

Municipal collection

Inert landfill

Recycling

Waste industry hierarchy of profitability

High margin (over 15%)	Landfill disposal
Reliable long-term returns	Landfill gas generation
Modest margins (less than 10%)	Clinical waste incineration
	Commercial/industrial collection
	Treatment of liquid wastes
Break-even or low margins	High temperature incineration
	Municipal collection
	Recycling

Source: Merrill Lynch, Pollution Control, September 1998

cost more to collect the waste and segment it than can be realised, always assuming there is some demand in the first instance. Thus quite a proportion of recycling activity in the UK is municipally subsidised.[35]

In profitability, landfill hits the top of the scale, while recycling remains at the bottom. Landfill commands high profits because, once it has its licenses and planning permission, it can command monopoly rent. This explains the economic dynamic of the waste sector, with a concentration of ownership of landfill sites and competition for low-value municipal collection contracts. Landfill, at the bottom of the environmental hierarchy, is most profitable, while recycling produces the poorest market returns.

It is not surprising, then, that recycling rates remain so low. Those who want it (the municipalities) cannot afford it. Those who can afford it (the private sector) have no incentive to want it.

Could this be different?

There are three main factors which could influence the economic viability recycling:

- current market prices do not reflect 'external' environmental costs and benefits, and should be corrected by government policy
- there are market imperfections in the operation of waste management, which if they were corrected would change the hierarchy of profitability
- the costs of intensive recycling could be lowered through increased scale and efficiency.

Environmental externalities

We already have detailed estimates of the environmental effects of different forms of waste management. Recycling, not surprisingly, produces the highest benefits, estimated by Coopers and Lybrand to be £114 a tonne, as against net costs of £6 and £7 per tonne for landfill and incineration, respectively.[36] Various instruments are being used that adjust current market prices to reflect environmental externalities; they do not reflect the environmental (let alone the economic and social) benefits accruing from recycling.[37]

The previous government introduced a £7 a tonne tax on landfill to reflect these environmental 'diseconomies', and the current government has increased it to £10, rising to £15 by 2004. It has also provided various subsidies and benefits to incineration:

- Subsidies under the Non Fossil Fuel Obligation (NFFO), currently valued at £7.50 a tonne
- Permission to realise cash under the packaging regulations for 19 per cent of municipal waste burnt, worth £4 a tonne

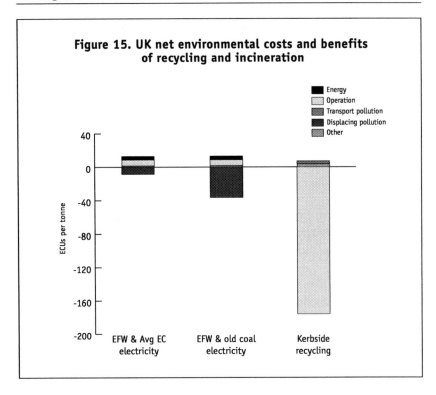

Figure 15. UK net environmental costs and benefits of recycling and incineration

Figure 16. Net environmental benefits associated with the recycling of different materials in the UK

Material	Ecu per tonne of recycled material
Non-ferrous materials	979
Ferrous metals	313
Glass	207
Paper	73
Textiles	70
Rigid plastics	51
Plastic film	-18
Average EU	170

Source: Coopers & Lybrand (1996)

- Classification of bottom ash as inert waste, which saves at least £2.50 a tonne of waste processed
- Capital subsidies under the Private Finance Initiative
- Exemption from property rates, which for the Edmonton incinerator was worth £2 a tonne. This is due to be phased out.
- Relative to labour intensive recycling, it also benefits from the normal capital allowances.

Recycling, on the other hand, receives limited support:

- *A recycling credit for 'monitorable' recycling valued at the cost of disposing of municipal waste.* As disposal costs rise, so does the recycling credit. Currently average English disposal costs are £36 a tonne (£25 a tonne for counties). Recycling credits are an internal transfer from disposal authorities. For unitary authorities they provide no incentive since they merely shift finance from one budget heading to another.
- *Producer responsibility payments.* These currently operate for packaging and require those involved in producing, using or distributing packaging to contribute funds towards achieving recycling targets. Few of these funds find their way into collection.
- *Capital subsidies.* Some scope for capital investment in recycling and composting by local authorities was provided under a system of supplementary credit approvals (SCAs), which was recently stopped. Large, capital-intensive composting processes or sorting stations would be eligible to apply for support under the Private Finance Initiative and, since the 1999 budget, both capital and operating revenue could in principle be advanced for recycling pilot projects under the landfill tax offset scheme. London received £12 million under a pilot Capital Challenge programme, and eligible areas can apply for EU funds. Since the ending of the SCAs, for the most part there is no general capital support.

The current forms of support amount to only a third of the Coopers and Lybrand estimates of the net environmental benefits of recycling. If further funding was provided to make up this gap (£76 a tonne) there would be an immediate major increase in recycling in the UK.

Market imperfections

The second factor is the distorting effect of imperfect markets. The most obvious of these is concentrated purchasing power of some material re-processors, notably:

- *Aluminium.* Alcan is the dominant purchaser of used aluminium cans.
- *Steel.* Steel cans are sold either to British Steel directly or to AMG, the sole owner of tinning capacity in the UK.
- *Glass.* Two of the three major glass bottle producer companies established a joint purchasing body, the British Glass Recycling Consortium; competition is provided in some areas by Berrymans of Dagenham.
- *Newsprint.* There are three newsprint mills taking recycled paper in the UK, only one of which is in the south. This gives the three mills substantial market power.

One reflection of this power is that increases in the landfill tax have led to reductions in secondary material prices. As economic theory would predict, the municipal 'supply' schedule for the sale of materials shifts down, because they are 'saving' more by recycling, and purchasers with monopoly power can capture most of the saving. In some cases this is even specified in supply contracts. Similar effects take place in the packaging recovery scheme, where any subsidy to municipal suppliers may lead to a cut in material prices.

If the benefits of landfill taxes and recycling subsidies are passed through to processors rather than collectors, recycling will remain unsupported until new demand for materials increases price levels. This depends on either the expansion of existing processors or the establishment of new ones, which has been slow to happen, for two reasons. First, there are substantial barriers to entry in fields such as steel, aluminium can re-processing and glass bottle manufacturing. Second, packaging subsidies elsewhere in Europe have depressed material prices, allowed overseas processors – for example in cardboard – to reduce prices on their final products and put UK processors under competitive pressure. In short some countries have used recycling subsidies to give their processors a competitive advantage in European markets.

A second area of market power, the ownership of restricted landfill, has raised landfill prices relative to other forms of waste treatment. The landfill tax and incinerator subsidies have brought the price of different disposal options closer to each other, putting competitive pressure on landfill operations. In other countries, increased recycling and waste reduction has led to waste shortages, reduced landfill prices and serious capacity crises for incinerators. However, the barriers to entry for landfills and incinerators in any one area (because of the need for licenses and planning permission) means that they still offer more chance of monopoly rents than recycling, which has a low entry cost.

The current cost and market structure of the UK waste industry means that recycling will only be attractive to private investors if it is tied (through contractual packages) to high return activities, such as landfill. Establishing intensive recycling programmes on their own is not, as we saw above, an economic proposition.

The overall impact of these market imperfections is to depress secondary materials prices and therefore to neutralise the subsidies on recycling collection.

Cutting recycling costs

If markets pose a problem on the demand side, recycling also faces problems of supply. If it is an 'add-on' service, any deficit between the collection costs and income from materials is an extra charge on municipal budgets. In the start-up phase of an intensive recycling scheme, the net cost may run from £20 to £100 per tonne.

How might these problems be overcome? There are three key points.

i) It is a declining cost industry. The fixed cost is the door-to-door service. Extra bins can be collected and extra materials added at relatively low marginal cost. There are economies of density (the higher the participation in any one area the lower the cost) and economies of scope (it costs less to pick up an extra material on a multi-material round than to pick it up on a separate collection – subject to vehicle capacity). The economics of recycling therefore depend critically on the capture rate of materials in any one

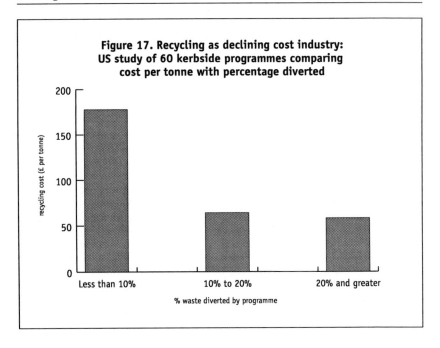

Figure 17. Recycling as declining cost industry: US study of 60 kerbside programmes comparing cost per tonne with percentage diverted

area (see Figure 17 for evidence from US recycling programmes). This tends to improve over time as a recycling culture is established. An initial scheme may start with 40 per cent of households putting out 40 per cent of their recyclable materials, which means 16 per cent of recyclable materials overall. Established schemes can raise this to 80 per cent and 80 per cent, giving an overall recovery rate of 64 per cent, and leading schemes push this beyond 75 per cent.

There are also economies of scale in sorting and bulking, management, and communication and information systems. As a result, the benchmark cost of collection and sorting for North American schemes is £70: almost half the cost of early start-up schemes. Gross costs for separate weekly collection and composting of organics are under £60 a tonne.

ii) Extra costs are often calculated for extra services as 'add-ons' – the cost of recycling on top of the existing cost of mixed waste disposal. However, the relevant concept for intensive recycling schemes is the cost to *the whole system*, rather than just of the extra service.

In developing waste plans with eleven Essex authorities, we found that gross systems costs for all dustbin waste increased by between 20 per cent and 70 per cent, depending on the authority. Moving to three stream dustbin collection, rather than tripling the cost, increases it by a maximum of 70 per cent. This is for various reasons: if waste is divided into three each stream can be picked up more quickly and there are fewer journeys to the tip or processing point; rounds can be reduced; once putrescibles are removed from residual waste, one or two of the streams can be collected fortnightly; sometimes two streams can be collected in one vehicle; vehicle utilisation can increase.

We also found that almost all local authorities could use existing assets at low incremental costs. Many have their own residents' newspaper which can carry recycling information. Equipment and depots from the highways or transport departments can often supplement those of the waste department and other overheads can be shared.

Equally important, the costs of managing many other kinds of waste, which in some authorities amount a third of the total waste stream, and cost between £100 and £300 a tonne, can be dramatically reduced by being re-organised around intensive recycling. Door-to-door collection on high-rise estates is one example; more extensive use of the special collection services is another. This is part of re-wiring the 'whole system', rather than just adding functions to the existing operation.

iii) Reorganising waste into separate streams opens the way for innovation. The following are leading examples from the 1990s.

Containers. Alongside new types of dustbin, the introduction of strong kraft paper sacks for organic waste has dramatically cut the weight of organics through evaporation, equivalent to reducing the weight of all dustbin waste by between 10 per cent and 17 per cent.

Vehicles. The post-war trend has been towards larger vehicles with more powerful compaction. Shifting waste into streams allows for much smaller vehicles; mobile containers for composting and feeder systems for bulk containers.

Management information systems. Bar codes on bins allow participation to be tracked, and bins can be weighed on vehicles before being emptied. Waste composition analysis monitors the effectiveness of source separation. Computerised routing allows collection rounds to be readjusted to the relative weights of materials.

Conclusions

Our detailed study of intensive recycling and composting systems in Essex produced three main conclusions.

i) The economics of recycling do not depend on markets, price subsidies or recycling credits. Even if there was no income from materials, at current costs of landfill, the three stream system is cost neutral.[38]

ii) The critical variables are the capture rate of organics and dry recyclables and the net costs of the three stream system (the Essex study estimates a 40 per cent increase on a single stream collection system). A local authority can control both these variables.

iii) An established intensive recycling system will cut overall waste management costs. With material revenues of £25 a tonne (a low estimate), the net system costs of intensive recycling cut the current overall system costs by 14 per cent. With the prospective increase in the cost of disposal, whether by landfill or incineration, (forecast to rise by two thirds in Essex over the next six years) recycling in all waste streams can cut systems costs by a half. This is Factor Four applied to waste management: halving disposal at half the system cost.

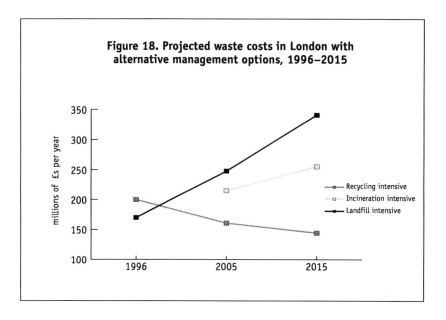

Figure 18. Projected waste costs in London with alternative management options, 1996–2015

This central conclusion, that intensive recycling schemes cut overall waste management costs, has been reinforced by Seattle and other leading North American programmes.[39] The Essex study also confirms the results of the London study shown in Figure 18. Intensive recycling initially raises systems costs but then declines to give a saving of 14 per cent on current costs by 2015. A landfill based system is forecast to double systems costs and incineration to raise them by 50 per cent.

These results are even more striking when you add to them the long-term trend towards increased material prices and the external environmental, social and economic gains of recycling. But even without these, intensive recycling systems demonstrate a strong version of the Factor Four thesis: system change geared around increased material productivity can radically reduce overall costs.

This poses the economic question in a new way. If we are right that there are these savings even without subsidies, why does the change not take place either through the market or through local authorities? Collection authorities, in particular, have even greater incentive to introduce the new system because they would receive recycling credits for it. The next chapter sets out the reasons for inaction.

Perverse institutions

The main problem is institutional. The waste industry is structured around disposal: its task has been to gather as much waste as possible, pack it as tightly as possible and ship it to disposal sites. The types of organisation, their histories and cultures , which play a major part in waste, have a profound influence on the way in which waste strategies develop. In the public sector, there is a strong distinction between collection (undertaken at district or borough level) and disposal (done by counties and waste disposal authorities). In the private sector, waste companies have traditionally grown from transport and aggregates or minerals businesses. During the 1990s, water companies diversified into the industry, bringing a culture of large-scale utilities management. But the industry's prime interest still lies in holes in the ground or chimneys in the air. Collection is seen as a contributory stream to corporate strategies centred on disposal.

The industry's roots have shaped its institutional and professional culture. Its training programmes, trade magazines, trade fairs and career paths focus mainly on managing fleets of vehicles (or barges), on equipment and logistics and on treatment and disposal facilities. As they have grown in size, their organisations have changed from family firms to corporate pyramids, part of complex international groups.

The role of organisational culture
We should expect this kind of organisation to have difficulty re-designing themselves around intensive recycling, which requires the skills of a modern retailer rather than those of a transporter of aggregates; a Tesco rather than a Tarmac. Intensive recycling brings new challenges

to waste management: in social marketing, household interaction, materials quality control and orientation to the needs of material processors. All these require new skills, new types of labour and management, and greatly expanded management information systems.

Private waste firms have, by and large, not tried to re-structure themselves around these skills, because this is not where the money is. If they do offer recycling or composting, the systems are focused on facilities: capital intensive sorting or composting plants, based on a traditional collection model. Developing a system aimed at maximising materials productivity would require major changes. At the moment, there is no incentive to embark on such a change.

Nor is there any incentive for companies outside the sector, which do have the skills, to enter municipal recycling. As the market is currently structured, recycling alone is not a viable proposition. The new service sector firms lack the knowledge and assets to be players in disposal as well as collection. And waste is not an image that consumer-oriented companies would necessarily want attached to their brand. All of these are barriers to entry from above.

On the supply side of the waste industry, given the way that firms are organised, major systems changes do not appear to make economic sense. From the perspective of their centralised business planning departments, there are limits to capture rates from kerbside collections. A three-stream system planned out on a drawing board seems to have high costs, and so higher recycling rates can only be achieved through mixed waste sorting at high-cost facilities.

In Germany, large waste companies were called on to develop intensive recycling, and they did it in this high cost way. They have replicated traditional collection systems (often running four in parallel), and expensive centralised sorting and composting facilities. The result – for the packaging stream – is a cost of £280 per tonne. Undertaken in this way, intensive recycling increases rather than cuts systems costs, but it has been justified and promoted because of the other advantages to secondary materials industries.

Creating systems change

So the failure to move to a smarter and cheaper system is explained by the fact that the main players in the waste industry do not have the necessary corporate skills or organisational cultures. This point is often assumed away in economic analysis, yet it is central to studies of economic transition. The old organisational structures will argue that the changes cannot work, cannot be afforded or won't make a difference. Their approaches to innovation are shaped by their structures. They stick to their guns even though maintaining high-cost inflexible technologies becomes increasingly difficult as change demands ever-more flexibility.

The problem of inflexibility is shown most clearly in the history of large energy utilities in North America and Europe, structured as they were round the management of power stations, particularly nuclear facilities. They found it extraordinarily difficult to promote energy saving programmes and only seriously addressed the issue when they were forced to do so by regulatory agencies.[40] The home energy efficiency groups were outsiders in these organisations, just as cyclists or car-sharing clubs remain outsiders in the corporate world of transport. They come from different cultural worlds, but effective new systems must find ways of bringing them together.

In the information technology industry, the outsiders of Silicon Valley have been able to break open old structures and create new systems to which others have to respond. But in waste it is not so easy. The smaller units that can develop smart recycling find it difficult to extend their role to transforming the waste management system as a whole.

The potential agents of change

There are potential players here, such as the collection authorities or local recycling and composting enterprises that have produced the UK's most successful household recycling schemes. Bath, for example, has been an exemplary partnership between a community group and a local authority. Bury St Edmunds, with its 34 per cent diversion through organics collection, depends on co-operation with an innovative local composting firm. In many areas, like Daventry, Castle Morpeth and Croydon, the waste manager has played a pioneering role. Seventy per cent waste diversion in Kent has been achieved by Wyecycle, a community group experimenting with new systems.

It is not that local authority managers, direct service organisations (DSOs), community groups or local firms are in themselves the answer.

Some of the worst recycling schemes we have seen have been run by DSOs. Many waste managers have found it difficult to re-orient themselves from mass disposal to light touch, multi-stream recovery systems. Not all local firms are like County Mulch near Bury St Edmunds. But empirically, new models have been more likely to emerge from these kinds of organisation.

Their advantage is that they are specialised and closer to the communities they serve. A good collection department in a local authority has a detailed local knowledge of every highway and byway. It has access to other council assets: communications, depots and equipment. Waste managers have often experienced recycling as a burden, but the municipal entrepreneurs among them recognise the possibilities. Whether alone, through local enterprises or through partnership between the two, there is scope to develop a view of the whole system and its potential for change.

Barriers to change

A number of factors have prevented new systems from developing. First, the division between collection and disposal has blunted the incentives. The increase in disposal costs falls principally on the counties and the waste disposal authorities. The financial crisis caused by rising disposal charges does not fall on the waste collection departments, and therefore does not act as a spur to the radical system changes required.

Second, the disposal authorities, being far from the frontline of collection, find it difficult to understand the newer systems: they lack the information and the instruments to do so. Capital intensive facilities may be more expensive, but they are more secure. It is remarkable to see how, when faced with the prospect of disabling price hikes in traditional disposal, public sector officers in charge of disposal nevertheless attack labour-intensive recycling strategies that offer to cut waste management costs. The issue is not one of individuals: it stems from traditional hierarchical organisations structured around control. Large-scale facilities appear easier to control and are more predictable in their cost than lots of different schemes.[41]

The overall result is that it is hard to integrate innovative collection strategies with disposal systems. Counties and disposal authorities, as in France, opt for incinerators and capital-intensive treatment facilities. Incinerators require minimum tonnage guarantees, which potentially pre-empts the waste from recycling. If there is a conflict over waste, the Environmental Protection Act gives the first claim to disposal. This tips the balance even further against recycling; once incineration strategies have been adopted, the place of recycling is tightly constrained.

Most disposal bodies adopt some version of the 40:40:20 model in their strategic thinking. They assume a maximum amount of waste to be recycled (say 40 per cent, which most think is unachievable), then incinerate the rest and landfill the 'outage' and the ash. The main focus then falls on ensuring flows of waste to the incinerator. Only those who have been blocked from building incinerators have thrown their corporate energy into recycling. Without that energy, it is difficult to achieve 20 per cent, let alone 40 per cent diversion rates.[42]

The third problem is that both collection and disposal authorities face severe financial restrictions in raising the finance needed for transition to a new system. In Essex this transition required an estimated £26 million of capital investment and seed money of £15 million over three years. This is a total investment of £41 million, a third of what would be required for an incineration strategy, yet far beyond the capacities of the authorities concerned. They are also beyond the means of local enterprises. The financial constraints mean that, for many officers and councillors, finding an independent route to intensive recycling is unthinkable. They illustrate the general problem faced by individual authorities: the difficulty of investing for long-term savings because of short-term financial restrictions.

Fourth, the risk involved in embarking on a transition is partly internal (economic and effective three-stream systems) and partly external (markets). Local authority budget structures make it more difficult (and dangerous for officers) to take on these risks than to lay off responsibility to a single large contractor, even at a much higher price.

Fifth, there are no contractual intermediaries (so far) who specialise in putting together partnerships of local enterprises that can deliver whole systems change. The Community Recycling Network has many of the capacities necessary to do this, in partnership with individual districts and firms, but it also faces financial constraints and lacks experience in disposal.

The prospects for change

So the new waste paradigm has not been introduced from below for the same reasons that prevent change from above: institutional culture and capacity, and the inability of key players to assemble the resources and allies necessary to change the whole system rather than just one part of it. Municipal collection authorities are constrained by finance and their capacity to manage risk. They often find themselves at odds with disposal authorities and challenged by the 'open systems' culture required for effective recycling. The enterprises that have pioneered elements of the new system are too fragmented and under-resourced to develop the full package of services and functions needed for a normal municipal contract. Because the economic gains at municipal level come from whole system change and have to be mediated through local authorities, the minimum size of a viable operation is a barrier to entry for the innovators.

These are not insuperable problems. Although much of the regulatory and financial environment is structured against them, 'beacon' local authorities, using Best Value procedures, could act as 'package managers', bringing together coalitions of innovative firms that included community enterprises and large post-industrial firms to transform the system. Seed funding for pioneers would be more difficult but not impossible. The packaging regulations open up possibilities for this kind of coalition. But in current conditions, such innovators would be sailing against the wind.

Given the extent of the change required, it is not surprising that Britain has remained so low in the European recycling league. The large enterprises, with finance and system-wide skills, find it difficult to produce the grassroots skills required for smart waste management. Small enterprises have, up to now, lacked the systems organisation to deliver large contracts. And municipal authorities have been torn between the old world and the new, unable to move financially along a path to which many aspire. This is the impasse. Breaking through it depends on the right kind of leadership.

Experience in other countries suggests that new systems depend on strong government commitment. Regulatory structures lay down the direction of the industry. But government itself is often caught in the net of the old order. If disposal authorities and large waste corporations find it difficult to deal with the detail of diversity, this is doubly true of higher tiers of government. For them, too, large capital-intensive solutions and centralised bodies are easier to deal with than a population of small firms. This is a big obstacle to changes that depend on diversity and multiplicity.

In the waste management revolution, the major advances have happened at relatively small scale. In federal states they have taken place at state level: German Lander, Canadian provinces, Swiss Cantons, US and Australian states. They have also taken place in small countries, such as Denmark, Austria and the Netherlands. Larger, centralised states like France, Japan and Britain have had more difficulty (and lower recycling rates). For the UK, developing a regulatory structure that can nurture a green transition is therefore a greater challenge than for most. But it can be done, as is shown by the abrupt change in France from an incineration to a recycling-led strategy. The French change was led by the Greens, but it remains to be seen whether the centralised forms of government can stimulate the economic innovation required. This challenge is the subject of chapter nine.

9. Disconnected government

This chapter argues that, despite formal commitment to recycling, there is now a great gulf between policy and practice in the UK, so much so that the government is on the verge of adopting an incineration-based strategy. A consensus has formed around the impracticality of recycling, despite the fact that it is growing successfully across the world. The failure to grasp the opportunities it presents is explained by the influence of institutional structure on policy formation, and by the difficulty of finding good knowledge and information in a diverse, decentralised, fast-changing system. If it is to avoid sending the UK down an expensive, unpopular and environmentally damaging route, the UK government must lift its sights, recover from a failure of imagination and show leadership in creating the conditions for the growth of intensive recycling.

Government policy towards recycling and reduction has two distinct elements. The first is to cut private sector waste through 'producer responsibility' regulations and the landfill tax. These are already having an effect on the packaging and retail sector and the construction industry. The second is to target municipal recycling. Government policy in this second area has failed. The 25 per cent target set in 1995 had, by 1998, become 'aspirational', according to the civil servants involved. The current English level of 8 per cent is an increase of only 2 per cent in three years. The reasons for this have been set out in the previous chapter: there is no money in it for the waste industry and there is little money for it in local authorities. The hierarchy of profitability in different waste management activities is the inverse of the environmental hierarchy, which the landfill tax has so far done little to change.

As a result, there is now a chasm between ministerial commitment and actual performance. The 1998 White Paper confirmed the priority of recycling over incineration, recognised problems of lack of municipal finance and materials markets and called for a concerted effort to overcome them.

> The government believes recycling is critical to the task of making our waste management more environmentally acceptable and is committed to a substantial increase in the role it plays in this country.[43]

But on the ground little has changed. For many local authorities the situation has actually worsened, with falling secondary material prices reflecting depressed international commodity prices and the impact of regulation in the UK. Many recycling schemes are now having to pay for their paper, green glass and even steel cans to be taken away.

Most seriously, it appears that the government is switching the emphasis of its waste strategy to a major incinerator programme. Formally, reduction and recycling remain the priority but, practically, incineration is being looked to as the most secure alternative to landfill. Instead of waste diversion being made the heart of waste policy, with incineration and landfill as options for residual waste, incineration is being classed alongside recycling as part of diversion, and planning guidelines and incentives are being structured to support it.

This means that the government is in danger of adopting an industrial policy favouring a high-cost, environmentally hazardous technology that effectively rules out competition for 25 years. The landfill tax was raised to negate the cost disadvantage of incineration. Incinerator industry expansion is being encouraged with a range of financial incentives. The Private Finance Initiative offers it subsidised capital. Local authorities have been told that they must plan for incinerators.

How has this happened?

Part of the problem is that Whitehall is still fragmented. The Department of Trade and Industry has strongly supported incinerators as a contribution to sustainable energy targets, despite the evidence that recycling saves three to five times as much energy. At the same time, they have given no lead to promoting a secondary materials economy, as in Germany, the US, Canada and Japan. The Treasury is reportedly unconvinced about the benefits of recycling, and other departments with an interest – from employment, welfare-to-work, housing, urban regeneration, transport, Kyoto and clean air targets – have had little apparent influence on the shaping of policy. There has been no effective *integration* of interested parties around a cross-depart-mental goal and, as a result, no 'joined-up government'.

Whitehall policy on municipal waste has centred on disposal and on how to deal with the consequences of the EU's landfill and producer responsibility directives. Despite ministerial insistence on the impor-tance of municipal recycling, and the House of Commons select committee's discussion of waste minimisation and resource produc-tivity, the traditional view of waste as waste, rather than waste as resource, is emerging as the determining factor in UK policy.

With genetically modified foods, the argument is posed in terms of low-cost high tech food against high-cost organics. For waste, the economics are reversed. The high tech option is more expensive, less flexible and more environmentally problematic, and yet the govern-ment is preparing to lock the sector into this model for almost three decades. How can this be explained?

The first part of the explanation is that this is not how it looks in Whitehall. There, the emerging view of the problem is this:

- The EU requires member states to shift waste away from landfill
- Municipal recycling remains stubbornly low and is unlikely to reach even the 40 per cent level allowed for by some disposal authorities
- The higher the recycling rate, the more expensive it becomes and the more problematic the markets for materials. This makes inten-sive recycling a high-cost option
- High growth rates in household waste and a growing shortage of landfill are creating a waste disposal crisis
- Modern incinerators are the only serious alternative: they are now environmentally safer and they contribute to renewable energy.

They may not be as good as recycling but they are better than land-fill.

- Incinerators are complementary to recycling and should be seen as part of an integrated waste strategy.

A senior civil servant at the Departments for Environment, Transport and the Regions (DETR) recently put this perspective to a meeting of the Energy from Waste Association (EfW):

We face a challenge trying to develop a sustainable waste strat-egy. There is no reason why we cannot look for a reasonable level of recycling but on a practical level. The evidence is that the best we are currently achieving is 25 per cent, and international statistics suggest that the most we will be able to achieve is 35 per cent. Although we'll plan for recycling, the total waste is growing faster than recycling rates and we do have a problem. It is almost inevitable that EfW will be turned to to take the strain.[44]

Intensive recycling appears impractical (confirmed by the Audit Commission) and expensive (confirmed by consultants and accoun-tants). Incineration may be more costly but it is now safe, it is a form of renewable energy and for the UK as a whole, it is emerging as the 'best practical environmental option'. This reading is reinforced by counties, disposal authorities, external consultants and many in the waste indus-try.

This is a coalition which confirms an old waste order. No new order can be introduced without them, and in any case they may be right. It may be that an incinerator-led strategy is the only practical option and that the challenge for environmentalists is to ensure that incinerators conform to leading edge standards. The benefits from recycling are attractive, but impractical for the task in hand, which is to manage waste disposal effectively.

But there is a nagging question that will not go away. Why is Britain convincing itself that new systems are impossible when other countries are already introducing them? Others are creating new waste economies and already recycling more than 40 per cent. Yet the emerging consensus, for some reason, seeks to deny this. A recent report by the consultants MEL, sponsored by the Energy from Waste Foundation, argues that the global saturation point for recycling is 15 per cent. For cases where this has already been exceeded, they argue that:

> The high diversion rates of 65 to 75 per cent reported in some Canadian programmes only apply to small, controlled demonstration projects where there are concentrated resources, favourable physical and social environments and financial incentives to the user.

Irrespective of the accuracy of this diagnosis, or of any other European and US examples, it is striking that we are now seeing reports and conferences whose main purpose is to show that a new waste regime, however desirable, is impossible. Any industry that spent its time arguing that change was impossible, and that those who achieved the highest productivity gains did so only under special circumstances, would soon be dispatched by the market. Without protection, competition gives short shrift to those who argue for the past on 'practical' grounds.

So how, in entrepreneurial Britain, can we explain the fact that a whole industry is arguing against innovation? It is not a public–private distinction. Large firms and private consultants have put the case against change even more forcefully than those in government. Clearly, some firms have an interest in the revival of incineration, and we would expect them to argue their case, but the consensus goes wider than this.

Understanding the failure of government institutions

One reason that it is useful to investigate these problems of transition by looking at the waste sector is that the benefits of a different approach are widely agreed. The long-run case for recycling and minimisation is indisputable. The problem becomes not one of principle but of practice.

Practicality poses a particular problem for government, because there are widely different views of what is practical. The old waste order argues against the practicality of the new. But a new wave of Green enterprises, environmental groups and entrepreneurial councils believe in the possibility of creating a new order and are trying to show through practice that it can be achieved. How can modern government judge what works in practice when the initiatives are so many and diverse, and so dispersed across the country?

Ways of seeing

In answering that question, we have to ask a more general question: whether different organisational structures produce different perspectives, and whether this has a bearing on how we might reconstruct government institutions in order to promote change.

The question of how governments can best 'see' what is happening in society has always been at the heart of economic and administrative theory. One approach to it has been to improve systems of intelligence, surveys and statistical techniques: the whole apparatus of 'surveillance'. Another has been to argue that the state can never know enough to run an economy efficiently, so control of production must be devolved to those who can (a Hayekian case for the market). A third is to change the structure of government, and its relations to the economy, in order to enrich the flow of information between economy, government and civil society on issues which require public action.

The question is crucial in explaining how government systems respond to or stimulate innovation. Four factors explain how the UK government has ended up setting itself against innovation in waste management:

- an orientation towards the present rather than the future
- its use of information
- the dominance of 'government by statistics'
- the relationship between knowledge and control.

The question applies not just to government, but to all the institutions involved in a sector. It involves the role and methodology of academic research and private consultancies; of business information and the trade press; of corporate information systems; of Parliament and legal processes; and the place of environmental movements and local knowledge.

For the change to new productive systems, and for environmental issues in particular, the private–public distinction is no longer helpful. A 1980s-style devolution of innovation to the market is not enough, since part of the private sector is geared to extending the old order, and the new elements depend in part on government to shape a waste regime in which they can thrive. The distinction between the old paradigm and the new cuts across the public –private divide.

Present versus future

The old way of looking at waste takes its point of reference as the present rather than the future. This leads to an approach that is biased against innovation. For example, in looking at overseas experience, averages rather than leading edges are invoked. The United States as a whole averages 31.5 per cent recycling, but it ranges from four states at 8 per cent or under, to seven states at over 40 per cent, and some areas within these seven reaching more than 70 per cent. Innovation is led by the speed of the quickest, not the average.

Another example is the use of life cycle analysis (LCA) to assess the environmental impact of different forms of waste treatment. Typically an LCA might work out the length of journey for recycled paper to a paper mill, or of timber from the forest to the virgin pulp mill. But if these estimates are going to be a sound basis for long-term decision making, they must reflect how each stage of a life cycle is likely to change over time. Recycled mill journeys tend to reduce as recycling becomes more intensive, while the timber journeys to a primary mill get longer as cutting goes further out to the margins of a forest.

This bias is decisive in assessing the environmental impact of incineration. As we saw earlier, studies which suggest that incineration has a more positive impact than landfill depend on the assumption that its electricity output replaces marginal fossil fuel power stations rather than the longer term, renewable energy sources. The first is short term and static, the second long term and dynamic. For the UK, decisions over energy sources in five years time are the relevant comparators, and they are likely to be nuclear or other renewables: on this basis, incineration loses its environmental justification.

The DETR is currently developing an LCA methodology for local councils to determine the 'best practical environment option'. But the method, by its nature, is static. It does not ask how things could be different, or how any one of the options could be made more environmentally effective. Other methods used to assess the sector – cost-benefit analysis, cost studies of existing schemes at current levels of regulation – all suffer from the same weakness.

Finding good information

The second issue is access to information. How can a central government find out what is actually happening? We have been struck by how little even collection authorities, let alone central government, know about the detailed flows of waste. The main information comes from collection lorries going over a weighbridge. But exactly what is in those lorries – how much from households, how much from trade – is usually unknown. Many landfills and transfer stations have no weighbridges. There is considerable uncertainty about the composition of household waste and. until the current Environment Agency survey, data on industrial and commercial waste was ten years old.

Equally, if we are considering productive potential, most councils have all sorts of hidden resources: a truck with a grab lift that could be borrowed from the Highways Department; some surplus depot space, or an old building in a park that would be suitable for composting. These resources can dramatically reduce the costs of recycling, as can innovations like the electric collection vehicle. But factoring them in depends on particular *kinds* of knowledge: usually local, informal and tacit. If these possibilities are not always known within a frontline council, how can central government be expected to find out? It is the old problem that FW Taylor and Scientific Management tried to solve by controlling the planning of production and taking autonomy away from the operators. But this is not an answer for managing waste. Waste shows the limitations of centralised intelligence in trying to asssess the potential of a new system which is, by nature, diffuse.

The statistical trap

Third, the categorisation of waste and the institution of waste targets has created a new form of management by statistics. As with all regulatory government, the focus is on classification, the status of each category and auditing the data. The DETR issues guidance on what should

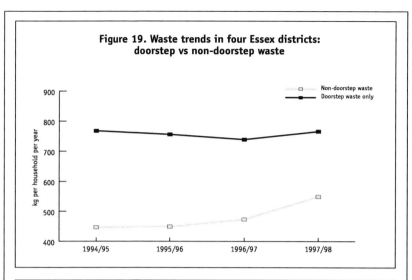

**Figure 19. Waste trends in four Essex districts:
doorstep vs non-doorstep waste**

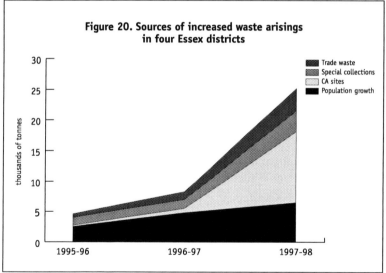

**Figure 20. Sources of increased waste arisings
in four Essex districts**

Measured municipal waste volumes have grown at 3% annually since 1996. This has been used as an argument for increasing incineration. When this growth is viewed closely, a different picture emerges. In four sample Essex districts, doorstep waste per household turned out to be stable. What has escalated are waste streams affected by trade waste switching to the free municipal stream since the introduction of the landfill tax. This suggests that the solution is not more incinerators but improved recycling services for trade waste and at CA sites.

be included in various waste categories and how recycling rates should be calculated. Formulas are produced to calculate trade waste or what allowance to make for home composting. When money is attached to such exercises, the stakes are raised. For example, disposal authorities have to pay recycling credit to collection authorities according to how much household waste is diverted. As a result, the formula for calculating the amount of trade waste in a normal collection round becomes important financially. One council makes incentive payments to its waste managers according to achieved recycling rates, and similar clauses are included in private contracts.

Packaging regulations also turn on these measurements, for example how much packaging has been diverted from disposal. Not surprisingly, the amount of packaging estimated by the private sector has gone down, and the number of processes classed as recovery has gone up. The government and the Environment Agency have held long negotiations on these issues, on classifications, eligibilities, measurements and verifications: a new form of economic regulation.

There are two problems here. One is how to apply statistical management to a sector where the information is so poor and where waste can so easily seep from one category to another. The second is the tendency for the statistics to become divorced from the substance and to serve not as a tool within a wider context, but as a realm of their own, with their own value and operational autonomy.

Recovery targets are a case in point. The aim of the targets is to promote waste minimisation and resource productivity. But this gets swamped by the politics of categories. Should recovery be treated on a par with recycling or below it? Is burning organic waste equivalent to composting? Should the low quality of recyclables from a dirty MRF or an incinerator be put in the same class as clean offcuts from a paper factory? Much discussion of waste in the UK circles round these questions of classification and value. Is incineration a good (recovery) or a bad (disposal)? Should landfill always be an outcast? There are boundary disputes, ferocious lobbying and international judgements on all of these issues.

Amidst all the noise, the underlying point gets lost because the categories are too crude. They start obscuring rather than clarifying. Each 'treatment' method has its own hierarchies. Home composting is better than central composting. Doorstep collection is better than civic amenity tipping because it reduces traffic. Landfilling unusable glass and rubble is better than burning them. Burning end-of-life paper fibres and printing ink sludge in a CHP incinerator attached to a paper factory is better than landfilling them. Seen in this way, it immediately becomes clear that the underlying problem is mixed waste: if it is separated, each stream can be treated appropriately. But this overall conclusion is swamped by the contest of classifications. The problem illustrates the paradox facing government. The kinds of system that we want to move toward use knowledge and information more intensively than any have in the past, but the kinds of knowledge they rely on cannot be captured and processed at the centre in traditional ways: they are distributed across the whole system of operation, embedded in its workings, and trying to aggregate and centralise them takes away much of their value.

It is only a short step from here to the 40:40:20 formulas of conventional waste management. Work out how much can be recycled, reduce landfill and there in the middle is a gap for incineration 'to take the strain'. This is described as an integrated package, a balanced approach in which each category complements the other. But this is only credible if the description is divorced from economic and political reality. To get to 40 per cent recycling needs a major change in orientation, in the way households think about waste and the way separate streams are treated. If a council builds an incinerator it confirms the old system and takes off the pressure for change. Transforming a waste system requires the dynamic of necessity. Where it has been achieved, it is almost always the result of the political closure of disposal options, the refusal of incinerators or of new landfills. Waste wars are the source of innovation.

Leading waste policy with incineration means that authorities will be lucky to reach 20 per cent, let alone 40 per cent ,diversion and they will be stuck there. If they expand recycling they will be left with the cost of 25-year incinerator contracts with not enough waste to burn. The 40:40:20 formula is falsely abstracted from the process of system change and masks the fact that incineration and recycling are in competition. They are not complementary: one must take centre stage.

Knowledge and control

Fourth is the problem of knowledge and control. One of the attractions of scale is that it appears easier for a centralised authority to control. It is cheaper to monitor one site than a lot of little ones and to deal with a few firms rather than many. The monitoring of packaging regulations is focused on the processors partly because it is cheaper to monitor. There are economies of scale in surveillance.

For the same reason, disposal authorities favour large facilities, particularly incinerators, because contractual and monitoring costs are lower. A contract with a single operator lasting 25 years is much simpler for a client than managing many small operators. For government, meeting a target for diversion from landfill with even 55 to 170 incinerators appears more manageable and secure than leaving it to myriad recycling schemes. When a civil servant says that waste is growing faster than recycling and therefore incineration is required to take the strain, he could equally have said that waste is growing faster than incineration capacity and that recycling will have to take the strain. Incinerators are notoriously difficult to site. Future waste scares and tighter regulatory controls may further restrict their future. But recycling seems less certain because it is not based on a small number of facilities.

The economy of control is a powerful factor favouring large-scale solutions over small. But as corporate organisations have found out, it can also entail less evident costs – the loss of creativity and motivation, of flexibility and of simpler solutions. From a central perspective, a simple solution may appear riskier if it lies outside central control. A nuclear plant, on one level, is much easier to administer than a whole population of energy efficiency advisers. But nuclear power has turned out to be much harder and more expensive than envisaged and has created its own problems of monitoring, decontamination and consent. This also applies to incineration. At the level of targets and percentages, it looks like a manageable solution, but it arouses public disquiet and opposition, it poses profound regulatory problems in controlling emissions and residues, and it creates its own operational risks.

Incinerators likewise have their own problems of organisational control. In the US and in continental Europe, for example, controlling what is put into them will always be difficult. As the cost of hazardous waste disposal increases, so does the incentive for it to find its way unlawfully into incinerators, just as landfill taxes have encouraged the migration of trade waste into the household stream.

The issue of control is the heart of environmental transition. Who controls what and how? For those at the centre of conventionally structured public organisations, the problem is preserving account-ability. But how can this be done without reinforcing hierarchy and restricting initiative? Can accountability and control be distributed rather than centralised, along with intelligence?

One of our over-riding experiences in developing the Demos waste project is the contradiction that repeatedly arises between the creativity of new solutions and the imperative of control. It is found in local government, where recycling officers try to introduce new schemes but are lodged at the bottom of a hierarchical structure (one London council we worked with had eleven layers of authority between the frontline dustman and the decision-making apex). There is no way that those at the top can know what is happening on the ground, and senior decision making is influenced by factors that have nothing to do with service quality.

Similarly in politics, the consolidation of power can easily run into conflict with innovation and innovators. At times it can seem as though there is a general law – that innovation from below will be halted when it becomes successful enough to threaten existing structures of author-ity. The larger authorities, and the more centralised the control of infor-mation, the more difficult the problem seems to become. Achieving real outcomes on the ground still commands too little weight.

These are general issues, but they often arise in relation to new tech-nology. While large-scale technologies appear to provide administrative solutions to those at the centre, they create real problems for those at the base. Environmental sensibilities are now a major political and economic force, and the response from the centre is tending towards imposing its solutions on a neighbourhood and criticising opposition as particularistic. Nimbyism is a concept developed by central planners to describe opposition. But opposition is often universal, even when it is focused around a particular proposal or cause. Roads protestors propose bicycles and public transport, rather than fighting to put more roads in the next parish. The same is true of those opposing incinerators and landfills.

At the heart of this tension is risk: who judges it, who bears it and how it is controlled. Managing this new economy of risk requires a quite different logic to that of centralised accountability and therefore calls for a new practice of government.

Conclusion

Government structures do not determine policy but they can make innovation more difficult. The French government, which faces many of the problems outlined above, has nevertheless embarked on a radical programme of intensive recycling. Its goals are to reduce waste, increase recycling, 'valorise' materials and restore public confidence. Its strategy rests on the idea of 'eco-conception' – meaning prevention and valorisation – and puts a central emphasis on the involvement of citizens. It is shifting the economic playing field in favour of recycling and tightening controls on incinerators. It is also advancing a programme of eco-design as a key instrument of minimisation.

The French programme, rather than talking down the potential for innovation, is geared to radical change. Many of the local authority plans were sent back because they relied too much on incineration. Public consent has been brought to the centre of waste strategy, along with the development of secondary materials industries. Goals are set in terms of the central concepts, rather than disembodied percentage targets.

Centralised government need not be a prisoner of the present. The structures of governance can be more or less open to change. We are now moving beyond the regulative, productive and neo-liberal models of government, to one where governments can act as a catalyst to forces of change in all parts of society. This new model requires quite new institutions for taxation, resource allocation, information and regulation. It re-casts the relationship between state and citizen, particularly in the way that risk is distributed and managed.

The UK's weakness in promoting recycling is partly caused by old oppositions, particularly between the state and the market. While the market has been cast as the sole source of dynamism, local government has remained shackled. Neither has been able to deliver the change. The

challenge is not to redefine the boundary line between state and market but to restructure the market and its incentives, to create a new interfaces between public and private systems and to open up the whole system to the forces of innovation.

Part III. Towards zero waste

If not this way, how? If not now, when?

Primo Levi

10. Waste and tax

Traditionally, tax has been about raising general revenue and influencing macroeconomic activity in the process. In the past three years, the waste sector has seen various fiscal innovations designed to change behaviour. The way they have been implemented reflects the problems identified in the previous chapters – imperfect markets and administrative systems. However, they provide new ways of thinking about the links between taxation and spending, and could play a central role in creating a new recycling regime.

This change depends on three main elements:

- developing the current landfill tax into a waste disposal tax that would reflect the environmental costs of different disposal options
- linking the new disposal tax more strongly to spending on recycling and waste minimisation programmes
- restructuring producer responsibility taxes to encourage the involvement of local authorities and small firms.

The landfill tax

The landfill tax, introduced in 1996, has had its proceeds used to lower employers' contributions on National Insurance. In the Green vocabulary, it increased taxes on a bad (landfill) and lightened them on a good (employment). The Labour government extended this innovation. Originally set at £7 per tonne for 'non-inert' waste and £2 a tonne for 'inert' waste, Gordon Brown has raised the non-inert level to £10 a tonne, and in the 1999 Budget announced that it would go up to £15 per tonne in annual steps of £1.

Hardly anyone has opposed it. Even more surprising, some of those on whom it falls (the landfill operators) have argued for further increases, something of a Chancellor's dream. The reason is twofold. First, by raising the cost of landfill it has gradually closed the gap in costs between landfill and incineration, something in which many waste companies have an interest. Second, the landfill companies have been able to pass the tax on to private waste generators and municipal authorities. In the private sector it has led to increased waste disposal charges and an inevitable incentive for fly tipping and 'smuggling' waste into the municipal stream. The municipal sector has not been able to escape in this way and has taken the full force of the tax.

Local authorities find themselves doubly squeezed: by spending restrictions on the one hand and by a central government tax on their activities on the other. Every local council paying for disposal has suddenly faced a steep and rising bill for one of its core functions. This year, local authorities will have to pay some £250 million in tax through their waste disposal function, on top of rising disposal charges. The resulting pressure on municipal budgets has led to cuts in statutory and non-statutory services, such as swimming pools and libraries.

The tax could have played a much more powerful role in promoting recycling if its proceeds had been fed directly back into it. But for many councils it has done the opposite and in some cases led to cuts in recycling, since this too is a non-statutory service. Its main effect has been to encourage a shift to incineration, particularly for urban authorities facing high landfill costs.

The exceptions are the district authorities. Here, an earlier provision of the 1990 Environmental Protection Act effectively introduced a forced transfer between local authorities. If a collection authority engages in recycling or composting and diverts waste from disposal, the disposal authority must pay them the cost of disposal they save. In essence, this was a hypothecated tax to fund an approved activity.

For a disposal authority faced with the landfill tax, recycling does not offer a way out, because every pound it saves through waste diversion by the collection authorities has to be paid back to them. The moment landfill taxes rise above the costs of incineration, disposal authorities can cap their payments to collection authorities for recycling. The tax has therefore failed to provide an incentive to counties and disposal authorities to promote recycling and reduction, and to address the funding of transition for collection authorities.

The wrong kind of hypothecation

One obvious part of the solution would have been to earmark the proceeds of the tax for promoting recycling, rather than for National Insurance contributions, which are marginal and diffuse. The Treasury resisted this because of their hostility to hypothecation. Instead, the Department of the Environment negotiated a *de facto* hypothecation outside the public budget. The terms of the new tax allowed for owners of landfills to offset up to 20 per cent of the tax on grants to environmental bodies for specified purposes. The offset was worth some £80 million each year.

These provisions amounted to a new form of tax farming. But unlike seventeenth and eighteenth century practices, which privatised tax *collection*, the new regulations privatise the *distribution* of revenues. One way to look at this is as an extension of tax breaks for charitable donors. The spending was explicitly not to further the interests of landfill companies themselves: like lottery funds, it was to go for specified environmental purposes like land reclamation, research, information and so on. But, unlike charitable allowances, landfill companies only have to contribute 10 per cent of the funds themselves and this triggered 90 per cent as a tax offset. Since many companies were reluctant even to contribute this much, the 10 per cent is often now generated from other sources.[45] The landfill companies have been given the rights of a charitable foundation without having to fund it.

So the Treasury's refusal to countenance hypothecation has led to a distributive system outside the state, in which private companies control the allocation of money to accredited 'environmental bodies'. Unlike most public grant programmes, there are no guidelines about specific policy goals other than those implied by the permitted activities. Project proposals are usually vetted by the central regulative body (Entrust). The actual funding choice is privatised.

There are three main problems with this system. First, the field of activity eligible for grants is too broad, with no focused goal. There is no way of judging the effectiveness of this quasi-public expenditure because its aims are so vague.

Second, the funds were not allowed to be used to promote recycling. This was changed in the 1999 budget, when support for recycling was explicitly added. However, this commitment has been interpreted narrowly in terms of research and pilot projects, and in no way deals with the financial needs of the recycling sector as a whole.

Third, it is unrealistic to expect the landfill companies not to use the tax to further their interests. Its very structure was an invitation to institutionalised corruption. Not surprisingly, there have been cases of applicants for landfill funds being told that any grant would be conditional on them modifying their business or public conduct in relation to waste companies (in one case the applicants were asked to withdraw from a contract tendering process in which both parties were involved).

The companies have also used the allowances for public relations purposes in districts where they have particular interests in contracts or planning permissions for landfill or incinerators. As one waste company put it in its evidence to the recent House of Lords committee on the subject:

> By encouraging community groups to bid for project funding, relations between the community, [our company] and the local authority have been enhanced. This has contributed to a better understanding of our operations.[46]

Similarly, waste companies have supported projects in tune with their broader strategic interests. Landfill money has financed a Foundation to Promote Energy from Waste, promoting energy from waste to school-children, research designed to undermine the case for intensive recycling and a glossy booklet and video sent to every council in the UK. The money has also been used by the landfill companies to fund activities that are properly their responsibility, such as professional training and landfill research.[47]

On the other hand, research from Manchester Metropolitan University has shown that support for waste minimisation has been minimal. The Chair of the Waste Minimisation Group of the Environment Industries Commission (EIC), in evidence to the House of Lords Committee, put it this way:

I find that there is great frustration amongst all of those I meet who have experienced the operation of the landfill tax rebate system. We and many others in EIC have tried very hard to obtain landfill tax rebates for waste minimisation and recycling projects with no success whatsoever. The landfill operators are clearly opposed and see such projects as a threat to their industry. They are very unlikely, it seems to me, to ever see opportunities for themselves in waste minimisation. This might even extend to recycling. The evidence in North America tends to show that recycling and reprocessing of waste for new end markets is an entrepreneurial business opportunity requiring flexibility and hence favours the small to medium-sized enterprises. The traditional waste management industry is good at managing fleets of vehicles and operating landfill sites. Since they clearly have major vested interests in controlling waste strategies, it is hardly surprising that rebates have not been channelled into the activities for which they were intended.

The scheme has now built up a significant interest of bodies with a clientelistic dependence on the funds. Rather than a transfer of an economic function of the state to civil society to achieve particular goals, the landfill tax arrangements have established what amounts to an environmental slush fund, which has privatised the politics of the waste industry, largely at the state's expense.

A missed opportunity?

Edmund Burke's financial reforms two centuries ago were introduced to stop practices of this kind. No modern government should allow them to continue. And yet the landfill tax opens the way for a new form of Green taxation that could play a major part in restructuring waste ecologically. It has had an immediate impact on private sector behaviour by raising the cost of landfill. It should now be extended to promote waste minimisation.

There is also a general lesson here. The 'good' use of tax revenues should be as specific as the 'bad' practices on which they were raised. Taxes on cars should help fund public transport, because this supports the expansion of an alternative that eases the transition from the old.

In waste this is particularly important, since penalties by themselves encourage waste smuggling and fly tipping if there is no other way out.

It is often easier to tax a resource or facility than to provide support for an alternative. For treasuries, National Insurance reductions are more straightforward than recycling development schemes. But we need new institutions that can promote development more directly, rather than through adjusting macro aggregates of this kind: one of our arguments is that new jobs can be created more directly by encouraging labour-intensive solutions than by marginal reductions in the price of labour.

Landfill tax reform

Four main changes are required to make the landfill tax do its job:

i) It should be converted into a waste disposal tax on the Danish model. Denmark has graduated charges according to the environmental costs of the method of disposal, ranging from £2 to £67 a tonne. Italy and the Flemish region of Belgium also use graduated disposal taxes.

The UK's disposal tax should be graded according to the degree of source separation and type of waste for disposal, with energy recovery introducing further secondary gradations. The lowest rates would be for landfilling inert waste and incinerating separated non-toxic streams with heat and power recovery. The highest rates should be for the landfilling and incineration without energy recovery of mixed non-inert waste. Existing incinerators should be exempted if they convert to source separation.

ii) Responsibility for allocating offset funds should be transferred to an independent agency. Landfill companies should no longer have discretion over whether to make the offsets but be required to pay these sums to the new agency.

iii) All new increments to the tax should be added to the offset allowances as they are introduced over the next four years. Any revenue raised above the existing level of subsidy to National Insurance contributions should be allocated to the agency.

iv) Offsets should be directed towards promoting recycling, composting and waste minimisation, without displacing existing support.

Producer responsibility: a new form of taxation

The producer responsibility regulations are an example of an 'outcome tax'. This goes beyond using tax to influence behaviour or correct the market, to using tax instrumentally to achieve a particular target. Outcome taxes have emerged during the 1990s in relation to environmental targets. One example is the reduction of sulphur emissions in the US and more recently the proposal for tradable permits in greenhouse gas emissions.[48]

These taxes have a number of novel features:

- A levy is involved, tied to the cost of achieving the targets rather than to a good or service. There is therefore an incentive to minimise the costs of compliance.
- Those who exceed the targets may be able to 'sell' their surplus compliance to underachievers. This provides a further incentive to compliance.
- The levy is earmarked to those who help to deliver the target but in a way that extends the concept of hypothecation. Until now it has meant either that a tax is set, and the revenue is earmarked for a particular purpose, or that a service is performed and financed by an earmarked tax (like the BBC licence fee). With 'outcome taxes' those 'obligated' to pay the tax are responsible for arranging the service.
- Money is circulated in the productive system independently of the state; both the levies and the 'bounties' are effectively privatised, with the state setting targets and playing a part in establishing systems of compliance.
- Tradeable certificates introduce a second currency that operates independently of the market currency, while being tied to it. Like any currency, it raises issues of the right of currency creation (minting), conditions of trading, transferability between time periods and the exchange rate with ordinary currencies (the price of compliance certificates).

- The targets are set over the long term in relation to a base date. This allows firms to plan for change as part of their long-term investment planning. The levies are ratcheted up gradually.
- The tax is not universal but varies between companies and over time.
- Rather than prices or government driving change, the impetus comes from those who pay the tax. In order to minimise their tax, they have a direct interest in re-organising the production chain and, unlike consumers, they have the economic capacity to do so.

These measures establish a shadow 'compliance' economy side by side with the real one. It is geared to environmental modernisation and centred round four institutional functions:

i) *The target setter.* This is a function normally undertaken by the state, with some industry involvement. With outcome taxes, setting targets becomes the main task of the state, along with monitoring validation systems.

ii) *The verifier.* Systems based on targets rest on verification of two items: starting points against which obligations are judged and levels of compliance achieved. For carbon dioxide emissions this means that it is easiest to apply the system to fixed immobile capital like power stations, since their emissions are measured anyway. Getting accurate data requires as much attention as financial accounting.

iii) *The minter.* A body has to be given the task of issuing certificates of compliance and putting them into circulation.

iv) *The drivers.* These are the taxpayers, who are responsible for achieving the targets. They have an interest in transforming the industry in order to meet the targets and minimise the costs of compliance.

How it works in practice

The British packaging waste regulations are a distinct version of this new kind of system. The targets are set by the EU and translated by the British government into collective obligations on the firms involved in the packaging production chain. The obligations are allocated between those manufacturing the raw materials (6 per cent), those converting it (11 per cent), those packing and filling (36 per cent) and the sellers (47 per cent). The contributions they pay towards achieving targets are like a negative value added tax, with the tax imposed according to the environmental damage produced.

The system works as follows. Each obligated party has to establish their share of the overall target in relation to the quantity of packaging they handle. They then have to demonstrate that they have contributed proportionately to the recycling/recovery targets, by providing the verifying authority with evidence that a certain weight of secondary material has been delivered to recognised processors for recycling or recovery. This evidence takes the form of receipts issued by the processors, called packaging recovery notes (PRNs).

Some of the obligated parties may have access to their own sources of recycled materials (such as the processors, who issue PRNs to themselves). But others have no direct access. They can either buy them from the processors or sign contracts with collectors of recyclable material.

The idea is that a shortage of a particular material in relation to the government recycling targets will increase the price of PRNs for that material and increase supply (and *vice versa*). It is a short step from here to PRNs becoming a currency.[49]

The problem is that the system has been introduced into an imperfect market. First, the 'obligated parties' grouped themselves into consortia. There are now thirteen, of which two account for 84 per cent of the 4,011 obligated businesses.[50] Then, the right to issue and distribute the certificates (the 'right of minting') was given to the reprocessors, many of whom, like Alcan, British Steel and the glass bottle manufacturers, already have considerable market power.

Because the regulations were imprecise about who reprocessors should transfer PRNs to, they are only automatically transferred to the thirteen compliance schemes of packagers. Local authorities and private suppliers of recyclable material do not receive PRNs unless they have struck a deal with the packaging groups. Overall, the system has channelled few of the payments from packaging companies to the primary recyclers, like local authorities, and instead has created windfall returns for reprocessors.

The potential for abuse has been highlighted by local authorities and by many of the packaging firms themselves. Given the inelasticity of demand for PRNs (driven by government targets), the processors have an incentive to restrict the demand for notes in order to raise the price. They argue that the notes may be needed to cover their own obligations. Even if they have to offload surplus notes at lower prices later in the year, as happened at the end of the last regulatory year, restricting circulation in the early months of the year further increases their windfall gains.[51]

As I argued in chapter nine, these curious arrangements were put in place because it was thought to be administratively simpler to deal with a few processors than with many suppliers. The windfall profits were justified on the basis that they stimulated the expansion of processing capacity. But the barrier to more recycling is the amount of material collected, not reprocessing capacity. There is ample capacity in aluminium, steel, white and brown glass and plastics.

PRNs are only relevant to industrial expansion in two cases. The first is paper packaging, which has faced continental competition from processors receiving materials subsidised through continental packaging schemes. The second is incineration, since incinerators have been allowed to register as industrial reprocessors and issue PRNs.

As with the landfill tax, an instrument that *could* fund the costs of transition has marginalised municipal and small-firm recyclers, and reinforced the market power of existing large-scale producers.

The problem has been exacerbated by the low declarations by the industry of existing packaging (7.7 million tonnes against the DETR's estimate of 10.2 million tonnes) and the large number of existing firms (currently 210) attracted by the windfalls to register as reprocessors. These two factors have lowered the demand for PRNs at the same time as raising supply. The current targets have largely been met from low-cost industrial and commercial sources, and from the municipal recycling that already exists. Michael Meacher, Minister for the Environment, has now raised the targets, and the latest DETR report on the scheme comments that household recycling schemes will need to expand to meet the targets, even though it notes that some collection schemes have closed down.[52]

However, as it operates at the moment, the scheme subsidises the purchase price of recyclable materials rather than funding the low-cost transformation of waste management in the municipal and industrial/commercial sectors.

It also promotes the incineration of household waste over recycling. The packaging recycling targets for 2001 have already been met through capture of low-cost materials through the industrial and commercial streams. Because packaging companies are interested in the marginal cost of expanding the flow of recycled material, rather than introducing low-cost waste management, and if the incremental cost of municipal and small-scale commercial recycling exceeds the long-run average cost of incineration, there are clear incentives to meet targets through incineration rather than through intensive recycling. This incentive is additional to the rights granted to incinerators to issue PRNs.

Producer responsibility reform

The packaging scheme should be restructured to encourage low cost recycling in the municipal and the small and medium enterprise (SME) sector. Four changes are required:

i) The recycling component of the recovery targets should be increased from 50 per cent to 80 per cent. This would allow for a doubling of the amount of packaging that is currently incinerated.

ii) PRNs should be issued to all those who deliver recyclate to registered processors. The processors should only be able to issue PRNs to themselves (whatever their obligations) if they have supplied the recyclate.

iii) A new, quasi-public brokering body should be established to minimise compliance costs and stabilise material revenues for recyclers by acting as an agent of last resort for the sale of PRNs to compliance schemes. A number of overseas compliance schemes (the Netherlands, for example) guarantee a minimum price for their recyclable material so that recycling is viable.[53]

Of the thirteen compliance schemes only one, Recycle UK, has sought to introduce long-term stability and to integrate production around waste minimisation. It only accounts for 3 per cent of current packaging recovery. The brokerage agency should aim to expand this model of partnership to most of the packaging stream, and play a much more active role in promoting low cost recycling.

iv) Incinerators should not be recognised as material processors. Their energy recovery is a salvage value and represents low level downcycling.

Conclusion

Following the landfill tax and packaging regulations, waste produces around £550 million in taxes. With the right adjustments to material markets, there is now enough finance in the system to fund the transition to a new waste regime. But the money is being poorly used because of the way the schemes were established. What is now required is to re-wire existing financial flows around a focussed target, in order to raise the environmental productivity of these early experiments in Green taxation.

11. Financing the local

Increasing the rate of municipal recycling should be one of the main priorities for policy over the next five years. Municipal waste is contributing to many of the problems in landfills and is now being targeted for incineration. Leaving aside construction and demolition waste, municipal waste comprises nearly 40 per cent of controlled waste: one of the largest untapped segments of waste as a resource.

The initial national targets should be those set by the Essex local authorities: 40 per cent recycling by 2004 and 60 per cent by 2007. Increases of this order, even in short time scales, are being achieved in North America. But meeting them here will depend on making a transition to a new system of waste disposal and secondary material conversion. How can this be financed?

Funding is needed to cover the transition costs of establishing an integrated four stream system of municipal waste management. On the basis of the Essex studies, we estimate that the investment costs of 'smart' intensive municipal recycling throughout the UK would be £1.1 billion. Start-up operating costs would amount to £200 million a year. The overall cost could be met by a combination of private sector investment and public revenues supplied by the increases in landfill tax over the next four years. The question is not the overall level of finance but how it is deployed.

A successful recycling and composting programme is marked by its diversity and a capacity to involve communities and small local enterprises in the economics of the programme. A financial package must provide for diversity *and* stability. The first problem is that the UK financial system favours large, underwritten capital-intensive projects over decentralised alternatives. Just as governments and the centres of large organisations have difficulty in dealing with diversity, the same is true of banks. It is significant that the small and medium enterprise (SME) success stories in the industrial districts of continental Europe had their own sources of flexible finance. Both middle Italy and Germany had strong traditions of local and regional banks, whose personnel built up detailed knowledge of local areas and people. These sources of finance were complemented by financial consortia formed by the SMEs themselves, including very effective mutual guarantee schemes.

The UK does not have this tradition of flexible finance. Its banking system has become even more centralised and de-localised over the past two decades. This contributes to the bias towards large-scale waste treatment methods at the expense of the new style labour-intensive ones. Incinerators (and other large capital intensive options) are financed on the basis of long-term contracts with disposal authorities, covering 70 to 80 per cent of waste throughput at a given price. They also have access to three other sources of revenue: medium to long-term contracts and spot market sales of electricity at commercial rates; and subsidies as the result of NFFO and the PRN arrangements. For financing large capital investment, this contractual structure provides a measure of stability, through the underwriting by the waste disposal authorities of most of the project.

An intensive recycling system, however, has much smaller and more fragmented capital needs. It is composed of many small investments by a large number of local authorities and is subject to greater levels of uncertainty. The range of investment projects and the need for local variation and for flexibility have meant that it has been considered inappropriate for local authorities to engage a single private contractor who might be able to fund a scheme of this kind. The mismatch between the flexible financial needs of an intensive recycling system and the kinds of large capital investment on offer has been a major blockage in creating a new, more efficient system.

A financial package would have to ensure stability and diverse investment. It would also have to enable local authorities to realise the potential cost savings of intensive diversion. The package should have two main elements: capital and operating budget.

Capital could come from any or all of the following sources:

- equipment leasing (covering 50 per cent of the capital required)
- private investors for particular projects, notably composting, and a share in MRFs
- development agency loans to small and medium joint venture partners as part of a long-term investment package
- top-up capital grants from existing public programmes (SRB, EU) and from the packaging recovery scheme
- existing capital allocations for waste management in district and county budgets
- local schemes would also be encouraged to make contributions in kind, in the form of existing land and buildings and use of equipment, that would be credited in any joint financial package.

Operating budget
This is the critical constraint for local authorities in developing intensive recycling. The start-up costs include the recruitment and training of new staff to develop schemes; the provision for door-to-door recycling and composting advisory services; investment in new management information systems; and the establishment of enhanced four-stream collection systems. During the initial years, these costs will have to be borne while some existing contracts are still in force. There are five sources of finance for gross operating costs.

(i) transfers from the local authority disposal budgets
Disposing of waste through composting, re-use or recycling provides large savings to local authority waste disposal budgets. Part of the operating budget for developing intensive recycling comes from recycling credits paid by the disposal authorities. But such transfers require the savings from waste diversion to be audited, and this in turn encourages the centralisation of facilities to simplify the audit trail. A few centralised compost sites are easy to audit (but have higher environmental costs) and receive credits. Home composting is difficult to audit and gets no credits. The needs and techniques of surveillance determine the institutions. A more effective way of dealing with the issue in non-unitary authorities is simply to charge them for disposal on a tonnage basis rather than through a precept based on council tax property value.

Second, the costs of disposal have put increasing strain on county and waste disposal authority budgets. Intensive recycling strategies should aim to reduce these costs on behalf of the disposal function, both by the quantities of waste diverted and also through cutting the net costs of CA sites. Currently, waste managed through CA sites may constitute 40 to 50 per cent of a county council's disposal budget because they are paying for CA site management as well as disposal. Re-orienting CA sites towards intensive recycling would substantially reduce these costs and help offset the steep rises forecast for residual waste.

(ii) smart savings
There is scope for making existing budgets go a long way to cover the costs of transition. Although much of the waste service has been cut to the bone, there are nevertheless ways of improving the budgeting of waste in a council, rationalising some services across departments, re-deploying assets and raising non-sales revenue. All these help to reduce the incremental costs of the four stream system. Examples include:

- some councils that still do not cross-charge non-waste departments for their handling of waste; once they do this it encourages reduction in institutional waste, particularly if supported by an advisory service
- waste reduction in municipal offices has a payback period of less than two years
- there are many best practice examples of cutting organic waste in parks, schools and municipal markets, and recycling highways and housing maintenance waste
- intensive recycling on high-rise estates helps cut the high costs of waste on housing department budgets
- using existing vehicles and assets more intensively for recycling by using them in off-peak hours, cutting back-up vehicles through changed maintenance arrangements, reorganising works depots in relation recycling and composting, using non-waste department assets for recycling and composting (schools, housing, parks)
- expanding recycling facilities for trade waste and sharing gains with the traders

- rationalising special collections in conjunction with CA sites to reduce costs and increase revenues.

The details are not important except that they are details and they grow ever more visible the nearer you are to the ground. Every waste manager and dustman will give many such examples: how consumer durables in good working order are regularly thrown out in well-off districts and then landfilled because there is no system for reclaiming them; how after Christmas there are many new presents in waste bins that are landfilled or burnt; how landfills close early so that collection time is restricted and so on. Every intensive recycling programme should aim for a 20 per cent component of smart savings.

(iii) materials sales revenue
One of the main factors paralysing municipal recycling is the problem, or more accurately the nightmare, of markets. There are two issues: the uncertainty of material revenues and their level. The uncertainty is at odds with local government budgets and their financing, and only adds to the fear of expanded recycling flooding the market. Along with financial limitations, this is the major giant blocking the path in the minds of members and officers in local authorities. It has got to the point, locally and nationally, where the fact that the giant may be friendly and going in the same direction is obscured. Moving from under 8 per cent recycling to 60 per cent in eight years can be seen in terms either of the need for an eightfold expansion of markets, or of an eightfold expansion of employment. The question is how to bridge the gap in time and uncertainty between the two.

The problem of markets is financial not physical. Existing capacity can take all the aluminium and steel that households can deliver. Paper can be exported as can textiles and glass. If compost is of the right quality then there is a wide range of uses for it. It is a problem of quality, rather than one of finding outlets. If there is too much green glass it can be stockpiled in landfill voids until new uses have been established.

For the above reasons, we do not need to fear the idea of mountainous stockpiles of secondary materials appearing. The question is the price and how it affects the financing package of an individual authority's business plan. Much depends on the steps taken now to expand reprocessing capacity in line with increased supplies of recycled materials. The prevailing pattern elsewhere has been to expand supply and trigger new investment as a result. The UK, as a latecomer to municipal recycling, has the chance to minimise the gap between establishing the supply line and expanding reprocessor capacity. Simultaneous investment in increasing the supply of secondary materials and in reprocessing will reduce the costs of transition.

However, for local authorities the initial shortfall in the level of material prices needs to be made up by funding support. This is better provided as revenue support than capital grants because it will encourage investment in the software rather than the hardware of recycling schemes. The finance should come from PRN and landfill tax revenue, through channels that also address the second problem, that of fluctuations.

In order to expand recycling, revenue uncertainty should be removed from the system. Income should be stabilised through an underwriting mechanism. Local authorities and small collection enterprises need access to the same kind of financial reserves that large materials companies use to manage commodity price fluctuations.

The alternatives are as follows:

Long-term contracts with a private sales intermediary that would guarantee the value of a package of recycled materials. Such a contract is often negotiated in conjunction with the operation of a sorting facility (MRF) so that the MRF 'gate fee' is lower than it otherwise might be because the contractor can keep the materials sales revenue. The problem here is that waste contractors themselves have difficulties with market fluctuations. They are waste management companies rather than materials traders and, unless they lay off the risk in turn, they are likely to estimate sales at relatively safe levels and treat upward price movements as a bonus. Any council taking this route should look for bonus sharing.

Negotiating long-term floor and ceiling price contracts with processors. The most critical material is paper. On the continent there have been moves to make long-term contracts of this kind between large newsprint mills and municipal suppliers. It suits both parties, providing security of supply for large capital investments and stable prices at levels that cover collection costs. In the UK, floor price contracts are being signed but at floor prices that are below the costs of collection and transport, and considerably less than the long-term price level at which recycled newsprint is economic. Any public financial support for new investment by processors should encourage long-term supply contracts with floor and ceiling prices as part of the investment package.

Developing marketing expertise and facilities that allow a flexible response to price fluctuations. It is usually necessary to establish an independent sales consortium of collection enterprises and/or districts/boroughs. The Community Recycling Network runs such a consortium, as do local authorities in the UK, the US, Canada and Holland. In Holland a grouping of 200 local authorities negotiated a successful long-term contract for their newsprint, having hired an industry specialist to act for them. In Ontario, the consortium negotiates material prices and offers them to its members. The advantage of the consortium approach is that it allows local councils and small firms to develop specialised market expertise, working in close co-ordination with the collection schemes and MRFs over the quality and category of materials, and being in a position to benefit from the long-term improvement in material prices.

The underwriting of a revenue stream by a packaging compliance scheme. This is the arrangement made between Bath and North East Somerset and Recycle UK. Recycle UK commit to provide a revenue stream to the council in return for the right to the PRNs. Alternatively, the PRN scheme could make up the difference between sales prices and an agreed benchmark price on the Dutch and Manitoba model.

A consortium revenue guarantee scheme. This combines the consortium advantages with the stability of underwritten prices. An independent not-for-distributed-profit (NFDP) consortium would sign long-term contracts with collection enterprises and councils, guaranteeing a minimum price for a package of materials. The price should be settled, as in Canada, on the basis of best practice costs. Any profits above this price would be shared according to a formula that would build up the consortium's reserves for trading purposes and also provide funds for the extension of recycling through technical advice, new initiatives or capital funding. The guarantee would need backing, essentially insurance against the fall of the price below a minimum. This could either be provided commercially or, more appropriately, through support from a packaging compliance scheme or landfill trust.

Landfill tax offsets have already been used in a similar way to bear the risk of soil remediation in circumstances where commercial return is uncertain. Guarantees could be paid in the budget year following any claim, which would avoid large sums having to be held as security and would meet local authority needs for secure payments. In terms of available recycling support funds, the advantage of the guarantee is that it would limit support to what was necessary to cover shortfalls, rather than funding the total recycling scheme.

Conclusion

Whatever the instrument, the kind of package required is clear. It should be advanced against an integrated business plan for the development of four-stream intensive recycling to include local and community enterprises on a partnership basis. The financial package should:

- provide capital and stable revenue funding during the build-up period
- give long-run price stability for the major materials
- comprise a portfolio of finance from different sources, including financial and in kind resources from the local authorities themselves.

Until now, local authorities have born much of the risk of recycling. This has been a prime reason why recycling has remained marginal in the UK. The difficulty that councils and SMEs have in raising capital to finance the build-up phase of intensive recycling is one reason why capital-intensive disposal and recycling options continue to be built, even though properly managed labour-intensive recycling schemes promise much higher long-run returns. New arrangements of the kind we propose would provide a major stimulus for extensing recycling in Britain. Local authorities cannot bear the risk because of financial and regulatory constraints. The private sector could do so – though at significant cost because of the innovative nature of the programme.

Most appropriately, the risk can be taken by bodies established to promote recycling because of its environmental benefits. This is why the first responsibility should rest with compliance schemes and land-fill trust offsets. Reducing the risk will both limit the size of revenue subsidy required and remove one of the main constraints that has been blocking municipal recycling.

12. A Zero Waste Agency

Any profound change needs an entrepreneurial force to drive it. This has conventionally been seen as the preserve of the market. But recently attention has turned to social entrepreneurship and entrepreneurialism within public institutions. They, too, have a key role to play. In the case of waste, it is striking that the one large waste firm that has made a point of working with the community sector to promote intensive recycling has strong links through its parent company to the 'new gold rush' of the Californian recycling industry. The private and community entrepreneurs representing eco-modernisation are, by the nature of this new economy, usually smaller and weaker. The sector has not offered the returns for re-investment enjoyed by some sectors of the knowledge economy. Nor do the eco-entrepreneurs yet have the social and organisational capital built up over time by small and medium-size firms in the industrial districts of Europe.

In other countries where recycling has taken off, there has been a mixture of private and public drivers. Strong political leadership has always been important. At the economic level, the drive has sometimes come from new market entrants from the non-waste large firm sector, either those which have knowledge that can be adapted to the multi-stream household oriented systems, or which have a particular interest in promoting recycling. It may be paper companies establishing their own kerbside collection systems, or soft drink companies concerned to avoid any take-back legislation. In Ontario the soft drink firms played this animating role, providing advice and financial security for newly established recycling schemes. Many worked through community and municipal organisations. When they did it directly, as in Germany, the results have been more 'industrialised' and costly.

High recycling areas of Canada tended towards a partnership model. Manitoba is a case in point. There the producer responsibility requirements led to a Product Stewardship Corporation, an arms length quasi-public agency run by a board drawn from the main firms involved in packaging, with government, recycling industry and public interest representatives. Its task was to 'animate' a waste reduction and prevention programme, provide for the economical waste management of specified materials and administer industry levies (the equivalent of the UK PRNs). It advised and financed municipalities in the development of recycling and supported market development and research.

In many instances it is municipal administrations and non-profit organisations that have provided the main impetus. But at this point the particular organisations need not concern us: the important fact is that there are some core institutions pushing change forward. They have developed the new expertise, acted as the go-betweens and given financial support to make recycling happen. In Britain, that role has yet to be filled. The compliance schemes could have provided the leadership but, with the exception of Recycle UK, have failed to do so. The community sector has played this role in an increasingly fruitful way but its resources and influence are limited. No hands-on consultancy profession has yet developed to diffuse the knowledge of the new economy. Municipal recycling officers are greatly overworked and have had to plough their own furrow.

All this again reflects the trading approach that runs as a strong undercurrent in the history of British economic policy (as against the German orientation to production, with its emphasis on skill and technology). If the markets can be got right, they will deliver. But this does not hold true with complex systems and complex processes of change. There needs to be a much denser weave of co-operation between the sectors, comprising players in each sector who can provide leadership in making that change. For the transition to waste reduction and recycling, the market has only partially delivered. The material processors have often taken the lead in establishing capacity. What has not happened is a similar dynamic on the side of supply.

We now need a new body to animate the change. Its task would be catalytic and developmental. Its form would not be a closed structure: it would work with and through others. Funded from the redirected landfill and disposal tax, it would have the resources and clout to restore confidence among those active in recycling. It could appropriately be called the Zero Waste Agency: 'zero waste' as an indication of its purpose; 'agency' as an indication of its bent for action.

It should not be structured according to the regulative tradition, burdened with procedures, classifications and rules of allocation. Instead, it should be created to achieve a set of outcomes and be judged by the success with which it does so. This means that it needs to be shaped as a developmental institution, working in the quasi-public sphere. What is required is an extension of the idea of social entrepreneurialism to the change in systems. The Zero Waste Agency should see itself as a 'system entrepreneur'. Its imagery should be drawn from energy rather than construction, from cultivation rather than engineering.

There are a number of guidelines that can been drawn from successful initiatives of this sort.

- They seek to change systems not through the introduction of universal, pre-designed alternatives but through the generation of multiple initiatives , through encouraging pluralism and creating networks among the innovators to act as a focus for expansion.
- Their primary roles are to provide a shared strategic focus, manage cross-boundary relations, support and advise frontline operators and set in place systems for training, information flow and assessment.
- They seek immediate ways to form coalitions in practice around particular issues that have been already studied and agreed.
- They favour flow over stock, working through temporary, goal-oriented full-time task forces and project teams rather than fixed positional institutions.
- They are not dependent on regulative change but take advantage of regulatory amendments that are in process, or work through special orders and the many levers of administrative influence within a given regulatory framework.

- Rather than pre-planning and detailed targets imposed by the centre, they work within a broad strategy that is elaborated and re-adjusted through feedback from practice.
- They need to be staffed by people experienced in the frontline rather than the back room.

Outcomes

In terms of outcomes, the agency would be charged with delivering on two immediate targets for municipal waste: 40 per cent recycling and reduction by 2004 and 60 per cent by 2007. There would be similar targets for the commercial and industrial sector, and for construction and demolition waste, following the completion of the current Environment Agency survey into these categories of waste.

Functions

A Zero Waste Agency would establish and/or operate the following seven prime functions.

i) *A zero waste tendering programme.* The zero waste programme would aim to bring forward and provide finance and advisory support to entrepreneurs from any or all sectors that had schemes to promote recycling and waste minimisation.

ii) *A 'waste academy' charged with developing the new trades and professions required by waste minimisation.* It would have its own premises but would also be expected to work with existing institutions, using distance learning, technical colleges and universities.

iii) *A recycling price guarantee programme,* which would underwrite material revenues for approved municipally based or local enterprise based projects and be run in conjunction with a recycling advisory service.

iv) *A PRN brokerage,* which would negotiate sales of PRNs on a consortium basis for recycling collectors. The brokerage would seek to promote long-term relationships between the 'obligated' packagers and the new wave of recyclers, encouraging the under-writing of revenues on the Dutch model.

v) *A new secondary material industries and technologies initiative* comprising a small staff of industry specialists drawn from the relevant industrial sectors to act as animators and links between the expanded recycling programmes and new industry. It would work alongside the regional development agencies, through a secondary materials task force. It would sponsor an international competition for technical innovations on waste minimisation as part of an international search for relevant systems and technologies in the UK.

vi) *Waste minimisation advisory services and development finance.* The task would be to promote ecological production through support for zero waste advisory services, provided both through individual consultancy and sectoral working groups (as in the construction and demolition sector). There would also be the provision of development finance for a range of waste minimisation initiatives and new enterprises.

vii)*The environmental body support programme* currently regulated by Entrust and run by the landfill companies.

The Zero Waste Fund

This would be a primary initial focus of the agency's work because it would be the principle means of tapping into and helping to resource collective intelligence around the problem of waste and its reduction. The past ten years have seen many innovations in the field that seek to use competitions and open-ended bidding to draw in ideas and people to carry them through. One recent example is the Architecture Foundation's Car Free London competition, which drew entries from over 200 groups – schools, colleges, consultancy practices, environmental groups – all around the theme of reducing cars in a city. Entrants were given access to a resource centre with articles and videos on international experiences. A shortlist was given £5,000 each to work up their projects and all the entries were displayed in a major exhibition. What the process recognised was that new strategies involve work and knowledge as well as inspiration, and the process was structured so that all three were encouraged. The Zero Waste Fund could immediately sponsor such exercises on waste free towns and cities .

Another example is the New Opportunities Fund, which has been created to encourage the establishment of healthy living centres and study support centres. These are initiatives to promote preventative health and out-of-school learning in ways that are open to the applicant partners to determine. These bidding systems, when managed properly, have turned out to be very creative innovations in administering social and economic policy. The Zero Waste Fund would promote 'preventative waste' in this way.

The bidding process would have the following features:

- a clear outline of the broad rationale and goals of zero waste
- an encouragement of partnerships between those who would be involved in the realisation of any programme
- professional promotion of the programme to potential bidders
- the availability of specialist support to bidders in preparing their bid
- a two stage process: i) an outline bid for which partners can apply for pre-feasibility funds of say £10,000, and ii) a detailed bid for which partners can apply for a 50:50 contribution to a full feasibility bid; this pump priming finance would be complemented by a time budget of specialist advice for both the first and second stages
- no restriction on who can bid
- where multiple bids from any town or industry are entered at the first stage, the bidders can be brought together to determine some division of labour between them or bring in other partners
- particular support can be given to areas of high need where project development and delivery capacity is weak
- projects should in general involve counterpart funding; the assessment of a bidder's counterpart resources would take into account the relative financial strength of the bidders in question and contributions in kind

- each bid should contain proposed means of assessment in addition to the basic assessment required by the programme; assessment for all parties involved should be seen as a central part of the programme and encouragement given to imaginative forms of assessment.
- the bids should not be treated as sealed bids – the aim in all cases is to ensure that a bid is as good as it can be, and this may involve consultative work after the bid is received (for example on the size of budgets and what can be done with given sums of finance).
- the panels assessing the bids would have lay members who may reflect the specialist knowledge and the social constituencies involved in the bid.

Multi-dimensional policy

One of the aims of the agency would be to encourage the delivery of a number of different government policies through the expansion of recycling and waste minimisation. To encourage cross-departmental working within central government, a fund of £50 million a year financed from the landfill and disposal tax should be made available for bids by partnerships of departments and the Zero Waste Agency to carry through multi-faceted programmes. These could include special programmes for:

- environmental task force placements
- traffic minimisation and sustainable means of transporting waste
- hazard reduction and residential/occupational health
- urban and rural policies
- the development of innovative environmental technologies
- a multi-purpose programme of environmental home visits.

Staffing

The key role would be played by recycling, waste minimisation and industrial animators. They would be recruited from those with hands-on experience, including those involved with intensive recycling overseas. The core staff of animators would be complemented by approved consultants working on a part time basis. Over the period of the first phase (up to 2004) one of the goals would be to develop a new group of Green technical advisers trained up with the animators and consultants.

Governance

The agency would initially be established for the eight year period up to 2007, with a review in 2004. It would be overseen by a board drawn from all stakeholder groups with an interest in promoting recycling and zero waste, or with skills necessary for the programme's success. Thus it would look, for example, to the retail and information technology sectors, to organisational specialists and applied scientists.

Conclusion

An organisation of this kind would marry the drive of the private sector with the multiple policy goals of the state, working with and complementing both. As well as delivering change, and working flexibly in pursuit of outcomes rather than according to fixed structures, it would be a source of knowledge creation. It should be a catalyst of innovation and a promoter of wider debate and the sharing of good practice. It would help set the model for a new kind of public agency, as well as playing a central part in creating a new economy of waste.

13. Democratising risk

Finally, alongside the practices and regulations necessary for a zero waste programme to take shape, we need to develop a new way of managing risk in relation to waste. The politics of waste exemplifies the problems of risk management that governments face in a growing range of policy fields. Scientific knowledge, for various reasons, no longer commands the legitimacy to determine policies that will win public support. Governments are finding it increasingly difficult to arbitrate and regulate in ways that spread risk in the right ways. The most graphic illustration of this is food and its growing domination of the policy agenda in the UK. A new waste regime would be an important opportunity for government to create and test a new approach to risk management.

One tension at the heart of the waste debate in the UK is the opposing views on the hazards of incineration. The industry argues that the latest generation of incinerators are safe and have eliminated excess emissions through improved technology. They appeal to science to determine what is and is not safe, and what is and is not environmentally preferable. This is how it was put by Malcolm Chilton, Chairman of the Energy from Waste Association, to the House of Commons Select Committee in March 1998:

> Any decision about which is the best option, recycling or energy from waste, should be based in sound science. I think we should have a strategy that leaves that decision open to science, open to changes in our understanding as time goes on ... public percep-

tion itself should be driven partially by a reasonable understanding of the science.[54]

But public perception remains critical: despite the reassurances about modern incinerators, there are still strong residual fears among people living near proposed incinerator sites. It is not just the older generation of incinerators that provoked a decade of protest in North America, continental Europe and Japan: the new generation has continued to do so.

So far, waste scares have been relatively localised. The banning of cow's milk on the continent because of dioxins emitted from incinerators never reached the level of the BSE scares. But the most recent case – the dioxin crisis in Belgian food, which was traced to waste oil from transformers that found its way into animal feed – is the first to cause a European government to fall on a waste issue and also resulted in the banning of all European food exports to the US. Despite new technology, incinerators are a generator of dioxins. As with BSE, GM crops and Monsanto's genetically modified hormone in milk (BST), there is a deepening gap between scientific assurances and public anxiety.

The German sociologist Ulrich Beck has argued that this tension is the defining characteristic of our age and that what we see happening in waste is part of a much wider development in 'late modernity'. He calls it 'the age of risk'. In his view there has been a shift in Western society from the problem of scarcity to one of how to limit and distribute a new category of 'latent side effects': the hazards caused by the success of science and technology in meeting material needs. He argues that the distribution of risk is replacing the distribution of wealth at the centre of late modern politics.[55]

As part of this process, science itself is drawn into politics. It can no longer stand aside. In developing responses to old risks, science creates new ones. He calls this 'manufactured uncertainty'. Operating as it does with probabilities, the worst case – of environmental or human catastrophe – cannot be excluded, nor can science determine what is acceptable. It can no longer act as the final authority, as Malcolm Chilton still wishes it could.

In part, science has lost its position as arbiter because its effects can never be fully charted. The US National Academy of Sciences reports that there is insufficient information to make even partial health assessments of 95 per cent of chemicals in the environment, let alone their interaction with each other. In this sense, we are dealing with an economy of ignorance. Even if we can chart them, by the time effects are observed, the technology may itself have moved on.

The growing economic importance of science raises the economic and political stakes of publicising what knowledge there is. In the US, only 7 per cent of known information on toxic materials is made public. When it does come out, its effects can be far reaching. The statement of a single scientist can now affect a product, or whole sector, more violently than any parliament. Given the uncertainties, and the high stakes, it is not surprising that hazards are a subject of scientific controversy and have given rise to a new politics of risk – of knowledge about it, its acceptability, the responsibility for its creation and of its distribution.

Beck's analysis provides a way of understanding what is happening in the waste sector. The epidemiological studies linking incineration with toxins and disease have by their nature taken so long to produce that the technology has moved on, and the results are dismissed. But then new facts are discovered and fought over – most recently the highly toxic emissions from the incineration of TVs and computers, highlighted by the World Health Organisation and downplayed by the UK. There is growing suspicion that the 'clean incinerator' technologies reduce toxins leaving the chimney, but re-direct them to the ash, and that in any case what works out on paper is always different in the reality of production. Politics even influences the way that environmental effects are researched and analysed. We need to look no further than the US EPA waste studies, whose 1997 draft, despite its academic standing, was subject to heavy pressure by the incineration industry in the US.

So if science cannot settle the question of waste hazards and the costs and benefits associated with their risk, what is the political process that can? A centralist response is to try and force through what is regarded as a solution, with the way smoothed by investment in 'education'. This worked in Lewisham for the construction of its incinerator, and in Cleveland. But in an increasing number of cases it is running into profound difficulties. The incinerator industry itself feels uneasy at pushing their projects through against public opposition. This is Malcolm Chilton again:

> I believe in democracy, so I think we should involve the public, yes. One thing we will not do in my view, having tried it on many occasions, is convince people living in the immediate neighbourhood of a plant that this is a good thing and get them to vote democratically in favour of it. That is quite difficult at a very local level and that is why I think that if these plants are required, then there has to be some form of compensation for living nearby. I cannot see any other alternative to it.[56]

This shows an industry intensely aware of its major problem, one that has halted the expansion of incineration in the US and caused most US manufacturers to leave the industry. It recognises that industry can argue its case before local people, it can offer some form of compensation, but that in the end building new facilities will depend on securing public agreement.

This is one of the emerging principles for modern waste planning: that it must to start from those at risk and work backwards. With mobile phones, individuals can make the choice about risk given adequate information. With waste treatment plants, like nuclear installations or electric power lines, there is a collective risk that is subject to individual choice only by moving out of an area. There must accordingly be collective ways of dealing with that risk, of allowing communities to make choices about how particular problems are solved, with what risk and at what price. This is what I mean by the democratisation of risk.

One field in which this issue has clearly begun to emerge is law. There has been a clear change in planning law during the 1990s, in the weight given to 'public perception' and 'public concern' in planning applications. Most notably, in the case of the Browning Ferris hazardous waste treatment plant in Newport, the court of appeal ruled that public anxiety could be the sole material reason for turning down a planning application even if this anxiety was not well founded.[57] In Beck's terms, the individual perception of risk has become a material factor in what should and should not be allowed.

There has been a significant increase during the 1990s in the number of judicial review cases about the environmental impact of industrial development, including many waste treatment facilities, that are increasingly bringing to bear human rights principles (and are embodied in the Human Rights Act 1998).[58] This parallels the link established in the US between the environmental impact of waste facilities and civil rights. What is emerging is a new body of law on the distribution of risk.

Public concern, and therefore consent, is thus becoming ever more important. The redirection of French policy towards waste reduction and 'valorisation' sets out, as the third axis of its new policy 'restaurer la confiance des citoyens et des contribuables'. To restore confidence of citizens and taxpayers. This is a good starting point. What follows it as applied to the planning and management of waste?

First, decisions on waste planning should be made at levels that are local and that can implement alternatives. This goes against the trend. Decision making is becoming progressively centralised. The DETR's draft waste planning guidance proposes that regional planning bodies establish regional technical advisory boards for waste, with a membership dominated by the old waste order, and even further removed from those affected by waste facilities. The movement needs to go the other way – to the districts. If districts were responsible for their own disposal they would have to weigh up the options for themselves, negotiate on an equal basis with neighbouring districts where they had no local facilities and decide for themselves what risk and what costs they would be willing to take on. We would move away from a position where counties seek to impose incinerators on unwilling local communities, to one where districts are made responsible for their own waste according to the proximity principle. The argument for centralising responsibility for waste disposal in the counties was based on 1960s principles of economies of scale. The 1990s proximity principle argues the case for returning the responsibility to a more local level.[59]

Secondly, we need a new economy of information for planning and managing risk. Risk turns on knowledge and how it (or the lack of it) is perceived. The problem is that science is a particular kind of codified knowledge. Beck points out that critiques of science therefore have to come from within the scientific community, from other scientists. The expert creates the counter-expert. Democratising risk requires that those who are invited to bear it should have access to their own scientific advisers, civil society's own 'civil service'.

Accordingly, as part of any planning application for waste facilities the applicant should be asked to provide, along with their application fee, a sum of say £10,000 for bone fide community groups to assess the company's environmental statement. For operating facilities, the licence fee should have added to it another £10,000, for those living in the neighbourhood to undertake their own monitoring and analysis of the company's and the Environment Agency's monitoring. In all planning matters where the economic stakes are high, giving due weight to civil society means creating the financial means to take independent advice on the existence and significance of hazards.

This is linked to a greater openness required on information. Environmental hazards need their own freedom of information act. Agencies set up to protect the public often end up closer to the industry they are regulating than to the people they are meant to protect. Regulative capture is a well-established feature of environmental regulation. Scientists move between the agency and the industry. Agencies take on the problems of the industry and try and solve them. The high stakes involved in hazards information encourage a culture of secrecy and a nervousness about public interest. As I argued in chapter nine, these are structural rather than personal issues: they stem from the ways in which institutional structure influences culture, and the influence of culture on organisational behaviour.

We need a new culture that turns the regulatory agents outwards. Public hearings, local authority select committees, rights of access to facilities and independent monitoring are all needed if confidence is to be restored. The flow of information and its processing must be reversed. Instead of it coming from the operators and being fed through by professionalised PR or managed public 'liaison groups', the public interest must have its own assessors, analysts and consultative 'spaces'.

One example of a different kind of information culture is the incinerator in Vienna, where the results of the continuous emissions monitoring are displayed on the street, side by side with the regulatory limits. This symbolises the turning outwards that is necessary for operators and agents.

Effective monitoring depends on six things: the knowledge of regulations; the design of operations to make infringement difficult; surveillance and inspection; the capture of infringers; their trial and punishment. In minimising environmental risk from waste, prevention will always come first, the design of products and handling waste that minimises hazards. But after that, we also need:

- regulations that instil confidence
- regular independent inspection and, where necessary, inspection of the inspectors
- strong penalties for infringement and compensation for those affected.

These are all elements in a strategy of restoring trust. Again, we have lessons to learn from the French. Their re-direction of strategy began with an independent review of emissions from existing incinerators, punishment of the many who were not confirming to regulations and tightening of the emission limits against which future operations would be judged.

The principles proposed here should be applied to all waste operations – to recycling and composting as well as incineration and landfill. The principle must be openness and transparency, not just to build public trust, but because they lead to improved practices. I have already argued that the new waste economy is information intensive. It also matters who produces this information, who has access to it, and who is able to read it and make it comprehensible.

The choice about risk must be returned to those who are asked to bear it. They are able to choose the balance to be struck between technology and life. They should bear the cost in deciding the direction. A new waste strategy based on expanding incineration, with increasingly centralised control of decisions, runs right against this tide of environmental decision making and will run into the same kinds of problems that it has faced elsewhere. Centralising environmental decisions generates its own risks, political and administrative, and its own unproductive costs. For this reason waste strategy must be built from the ground up. The government's task is to ensure that localities take responsibility for their own waste. That is the point of district waste plans. They should ensure that there is full and open information and the resources to interpret it. And there should be a regulatory regime that is seen to turn outwards to those it is intended to protect, not inwards to those who are being regulated. Along with a revised tax structure, new financing mechanisms and an 'animating' agency, decentralising decisions on waste will give the fourth major boost to the expansion of recycling in Britain.

14. A programme for zero waste

29 April 1999

SACRAMENTO The California Integrated Waste Management
Board, the state's primary recycling agency, formally determined
that in 1995 the City of Huron kept 52 percent of its waste out
of landfills, while Orange Cove recycled 88 percent of its waste.
'On behalf of the Board I'm pleased to acknowledge the hard
work these Fresno County communities have done to divert
trash from landfills,' said Waste Board Chairman Dan Eaton.
'Their efforts have helped California keep 117 million tons of
waste out of landfills since 1990. With their continued work and
the help of all California cities and counties, we can reach the
50 percent recycling mark next year.' To date, the board has
determined the 1995 and 1996 diversion rates for 304 cities and
counties. Of those, 66 at the end of 1996 had already met or
surpassed the 50 percent recycling mark for 2000.

California, the home of Silicon Valley, is now in the vanguard of environmental transformation. The leading areas are calling for 'zero waste',
as they are in Canberra, Australia, and New Zealand. Zero waste is the
approach adopted for the end of water pollution: 'to reduce with the
aim of eliminating those substances which are toxic, persistent and bio-
accumulative', in the words of the Oslo/Paris (OSPAR) Convention on the
North Sea, within one generation.[60] If that can be set for the sea, why
not for land?

If a generation is 25 years, the leaders in recycling are well on their way within ten. The Californian waste diversion law was passed in 1989 and within seven years nearly a quarter of its municipalities had reached 50 per cent. Nova Scotia is on target to do it in five years. Holland has reached 72 per cent nationwide and is still rising.

This is long-term thinking. But 25 years is also the length of an incinerator contract. Both invite us to think generationally. But the difference between the two could not be sharper. One seeks 'to reduce with the aim of eliminating', the other freezes a technology and the level of waste that has to go into it.

Even so, 50 per cent recycling seems a long way off in a country that aspires to 25 per cent and has achieved only 8 per cent. While economic transformation has happened in some branches of the cultural and knowledge industries, it has not yet happened in waste.

Yet the tide is turning. The leading European recyclers are setting benchmarks for European waste regulation, and this in turn is shaping the UK. Germany has shown how strong laws can reduce waste. Awareness of waste hazards is growing. Judging by the opinion polls and protests, an incinerator strategy would be peddling uphill, while recycling would be peddling down. If waste is managed democratically, recycling becomes the most practical alternative.

But how do we get there? Ten steps, taken together, would propel the UK into the Californian league.

1. The economic playing field must be rebalanced. The hierarchy of profitability must match the environmental hierarchy. This can be done by **revising waste taxes and public benefits** in three ways:

   - introducing a disposal tax that reflects the environmental hierarchy
   - cutting the subsidies presently given to incineration
   - introducing a price guarantee scheme for recycled materials to fund the build-up costs of four stream recycling

2. The £550 million raised in waste taxes must be re-channelled to a **Zero Waste Fund**. This requires:

- a change in the landfill tax regulations so that the 20 per cent offsets are paid into the publicly-run recycling fund
- earmarking a further 20 per cent to support employment and environmental goals through recycling
- amending the packaging recovery regulations so that payments by the 'obligated parties' are channelled to recycling collectors.

3. Establishing a **Zero Waste Agency** to administer the transitional funds and 'animate' the change.

4. Founding a new type of **Green Academy**, equivalent to the German technical schools of the mid-nineteenth century. It would be charged with developing organisational forms, knowledge and skills relevant to zero waste, and new ways of generating 'distributed intelligence'. Its curricula and priorities would be set by the needs thrown up by the new environmental systems. Hence its research, teaching and skill formation would be linked closely to ground level projects – following the approach of the Ulm School of Design – and provide learning resources to those in or outside employment.

5. Appointing **Zero Waste Advisers** – some recruited from leading recycling and reduction projects overseas – to advise on recycling schemes and projects. The group would be part of an international network, promoting exchanges and part-time attachments, and linking into practitioners' associations.

6. The launch of a **'Closed Loop Industrialisation' Initiative**, promoting the development of secondary materials industries, eco-design and hazard reduction technologies. In addition to material productivity, it would aim to promote 'de-scaling' technologies suitable for local and regional economies. It would be organised in conjunction with regional development agencies.

7. The extension of **producer responsibility** into new fields, not only electrical and electronics appliances, end-of-life vehicles and

tyres, but other durable equipment, newspapers, and hazardous products and materials. The weight of responsibility should be placed at the point of product and process design, since they have the greatest capacity to develop alternatives. In each case, the finance contributed by producers should be re-channelled to develop the alternatives.

8. **Devolving responsibility for waste disposal to districts**, through direct payments for the costs of disposal (rather than property-based precepts) and giving districts responsibility for identifying and negotiating disposal options within their own boundaries or with neighbouring districts. This would represent the proximity principle with teeth.

9. **Restoring public confidence in waste management and democratising risk** through: planning reform to give financial support and access to information to civil groups and neighbourhoods affected by waste proposals; a new culture of openness in regulatory bodies; an independent waste hazards control advisory body and an environmental freedom of information provision.

10. **A government-led commitment to the zero waste target 'within a generation'**, reflected in the above measures and the adoption of tighter targets to 'reduce with the aim of eliminating' mixed waste disposal by 2010. This would include a phased ban on organic waste in landfills, and on landfilling or incinerating hazard producing materials, and a moratorium of new mixed waste incinerators for five years.

Conclusion

One of Britain's major problems in embracing the new industrial revolution is its centralised government. It can make innovation in sectors centred around state regulation more difficult. But as France is now showing, centralised government, because of its power, can play a decisive role in setting directions and has both the responsibility and the power to shape the transformation of environmental systems.

The challenge, however, is the one that has been the theme of this book: how an economy built around highly centralised organisational forms in the private and the public sectors can open itself up to the polycentric challenges of the new world of waste. The UK government has taken radical steps in constitutional devolution and establishing new regional bodies. A zero waste programme would take this change a step further and, in doing so, would create economic, social and environmental opportunities that no government should ignore.

Notes

1. Incineration has been identified as the main source of dioxins in many countries, including the USA, Japan and European Countries. AKD Liem and JA van Zorge, 'Dioxin and Related Compounds: Status and Regulatory Aspects', *Environmental Science and Pollution Research*, 2 (1) 1995, pp 46-56.

2. A summary of studies on the toxic effects of landfills is given in *Rachel's Environment and Health Weekly*, #617 September 24 1998. For UK evidence see: HMP Fielder and others, *Report on the health of residents living near the Nant-Y Gwyddon landfill site using available data*, (Cardiff, Wales: Welsh Combined Centres for Public Health: 1997) and M Vrijheid, B Armstrong and others, *Potential Human Health Effects of Landfill Sites; Report to the North West Region of the Environment Agency*, London School of Hygiene and Tropical Medicine March 1998. For a survey of evidence on the toxic impact of incinerators see *Rachel's Environment Weekly*, 2 April 1998, and for the UK P Elliott and others, 'Cancer incidence near municipal solid waste incinerators in Great Britain,' *British Journal of Cancer*, vol 73 (1996), pp 702-710 This showed, on the basis of 14 million people living near 72 incinerators in Britain, that those living within 7.5 kilometres (4.6 miles) of a municipal waste incinerator have an increased likelihood of getting several different cancers.

3. See G Gardner and P Sampat, *Mind over Matter: Recasting the Role of Materials in our Lives*, Worldwatch Paper no 144, December 1998, Worldwatch Institute, Washington DC.

4. Surrey County Council have recently announced (June 1999) a £1 billion contract with the French company Sita, to handle Surrey's 500,000 tonnes of waste over 25 years.

5. International Institute for Environment and Development, *Towards a Sustainable Paper Cycle*, London 1996.

6. Quoted in Timothy Luke, 'Environmentality as Green Governmentality' in: E Darier (ed) *Discources of the Environment*, Blackwell, 1999, an article which contains an interesting discussion of the role of environmental policy in international geo-economic strategies in the US and Japan.

7. The Clean Japan Center, *The Development of Recycling Technologies*, 1997. The Clean Japan Center was established by MITI in conjunction with industry to be 'a national center aimed at developing a recycling oriented community in

the 21st century'.

8. For a technical discussion of incineration see Paul T Williams, *Waste Treatment and Disposal*, Wiley, 1998, ch6.

9. Pyrolysis still faces problems in dealing with mixed waste and materials such as PVC, which produces hydrochloric acid and chlorinated hydrocarbons in the process. Hydrochloric acid needs to be removed from the pyrolysis gases, but this process in turn can result in the formation of dioxins. As a technology this faces both technical and financial problems. As of 1998, the only pyrolysis plant in use is the Fuji-Recycling pilot plant in Aioi, Japan with a capacity of 1,000 tonnes per year; see Van der Naald and Thorpe, op cit.

10. As with all such processes it is information that is as important as equipment. The traditional waste system in the UK is information poor. Waste is handled in bulk and weighed once (if at all) over the weighbridge at a landfill site or incinerator. Forty per cent of landfill sites still lack a weighbridge. The DETR recently revised upwards its estimates of municipal waste from 20 to 26 million tonnes per year, and even at local level there are still no accurate figures on the different components of this waste.

11. Xerox has now opened a plant in New York that deconstructs all its machines, recycles the plastics and builds the new machines out of the pellets produced. BMW have installed a disassembly line near Munich that revolutionises the recycling of cars. Commercial and industrial buildings are now constructed to be recyclable.

12. The principles of ecological design can be summarised as follows:
– material economy

– miniaturisation
– durability
– recyclability
– reparability
– re-usability
– modularisation
– maintainability
– adaptability
– safety

13. United States Environmental Protection Agency 'Greenhouse Gas Emissions from Municipal Waste Management' 1997, EPA 530-R-97-010 . The research was led by the EPA's Office of Policy and Office of Solid Waste. It went through three major review cycles, which included additional EPA offices, the US Dept of Energy, the Forest Service and the Department of Agriculture) various trade associations; the Integrated Waste Services Association; the Argonne National Laboratory, the National Renewable Energy Lab, and various universities, consultancies and state departments. There was heavy pressure on the last round of review from the incineration industry that led to some change of assumptions and a reversal of the 1997 result that incineration caused slightly more GHG emissions than landfilling, but the overwhelming advantage of recycling remained robust.

14. 'Evergreen: from shoddy manufacture to textile recycling', *ENDS Report* 243, April 1995.

15. An argument has been advanced by proponents of incineration, that in spite of the overwhelming energy savings of recycling, incineration is more sustainable and should be promoted. The argument made is that UK recycled production uses fossil fuel energy, while primary paper comes principally from

Scandinavia and draws on renewable energy sources (bio mass and hydro).

There are two difficulties with this argument. First, it would freeze any UK industrial development that did not produce more power than it consumed relative to economies which have a developed renewable sector. A static view might suggest that all energy intensive industrial production should be concentrated in countries that already have extensive renewables. A dynamic approach would see the UK developing sustainable energy sources of its own coupled with energy saving industrial processes. From this latter perspective a modern paper recycling plant is a paradigm of cleaner production. Aylesford produce a portion of their own energy needs through incinerating old and damaged fibres; they are now off the grid and use natural gas

Second, although Sweden uses only 5 per cent fossil fuel in its power supplies, with the bulk coming from hydro and nuclear, Finland has a greater dependence (37 per cent). The pulp and paper industry there accounts for 10 million tones of CO_2 emissions annually (equivalent to 3.64 million cars on the road). Moreover, in each case opposition to nuclear fuel, raises pressure for increased long-run fossil fuel generation, which recycling would reduce. Savings in transport costs through recycling is a further factor cutting energy use and emissions.

16. The estimates are derived from studies undertaken by members of the project of the composition of waste in 25 local authorities. See note 23.

17. LPAC adopted the strategy of intensive recycling and a moratorium on incineration in February 1998. The full report on the basis of which the decision was made was published as *Re-Inventing Waste: Towards a London Waste Strategy*, Ecologika, 1998.

18. London Waste Ltd, Edmonton Energy from Waste Facility, Sixth Stream Extension. Project Description and Environmental Information for Consent Application under Section 36 of the Electricity Act 1989, 1998.

19. Total Edmonton emissions of releases of recognised or suspected respiratory system toxics in 1996 were 2,322 tonnes, 59 per cent of the London total. See Environment Agency Emissions data in Friends of the Earth Factory Watch website.

20. The Metropolitan Transport Research Unit, Transport and Waste Management in London, LPWAP, 1997 reprinted in *Re-Inventing Waste*, Ecologika, 1998.

21. For a discussion of the problem of waste on estates and the experience of high rise recycling see *Re-Inventing Waste*, op cit, ch9.

22. A growing problem over the past three years has been fly tipping, which 60 per cent of local authorities have reported to be on the increase since the introduction of the landfill tax. The fall in commodity prices has also had an effect on the disposal cost of cars, so that abandoned vehicles in the countryside have been a particular problem. A recycling system for bulky waste would make a major contribution to reducing the pressure to fly tip.

23. These estimates are derived from a model of dustbin waste based on analyses of weighed local authority tonnages together with 25 waste composition studies undertaken at different times of the year from a sample of low rise and high rise housing, in urban and rural

areas. Samples of waste from each authority were hand-sorted into 38 categories and then adjusted for materials collected through recycling, estimated home composting and at the CA sites.

24. For details of the office recycling pilots undertaken in large municipal offices as part of the London project see: *The Green Workplace Report on Office Recycling in London*, LPWAP 1997.

25. Jaakko Poyry and CSERGE, *Recycle or Incinerate? The Future for Used Newspapers*, BNMA, 1995

26. ibid, II.13.

27. Centre for Alternative Social Analysis and the Economic Council of the Labour Movement, *Improving the Environment and Promoting Employment in Denmark*, Copenhagen 1995, section III.4.

28. The CRN do however have many examples of cases where their voluntary status has been an advantage. One such was in the extension of recycling into Manchester Airport, where the cleaners of the incoming planes only agreed to co-operate with the scheme because it was run by a community organisation.

29. LPWAP for Demos and the Government Office for London, *Secondary Materials and the Rise of the Closed Loop Economy*, Part 1, Paper. 1997.

30. Another large mill under community control is in Kapuskasing in the north of Ontario where a town saved its branch plant mill that was to be closed by the US parent, and brought in a Quebec paper company to run it. It has now become one of the lowest cost producers in North America, taking used newspapers up by the same train that takes the finished newsprint to US markets.

31. The ban was the result of an international campaign triggered by the dumping of 4,000 tonnes of Philadelphia toxic incinerator ash on a beach in Haiti. The US, half of whose waste exports go to Latin America, has refused to ratify the ban. See:Rachel's Environment and Health Weekly, 595, April 23rd 1998.

32. Trevor Evans, *Waste Recycling in Germany*, LPWAP, March 1997, page 6, note 8, reprinted in Re-Inventing Waste, op cit, Annex 2.

33. On the contrast between Liberal and Fabian approaches to welfare in the early twentieth century see Peter Clarke, *Liberals and Social Democrats*, Cambridge UP, 1978.

34. W Kandinsky, 'And, Some Remarks on Synthetic Art' in his *Complete Writings on Art*, vol 2 (1922-1943), K Lindsay and P Vergo (eds), 1982, cited in U Beck, *The Re-Invention of Politics*, Polity Press, 1997

35. Merrill Lynch, *Pollution Control*, September 1998, p7

36. Coopers and Lybrand, 1996, *Cost-Benefit Analysis of the Different Municipal Solid Waste Management Systems: Objectives and instruments for the year 2000*, European Commission DGXI, Brussels.

37. Incineration only produces a positive effect when it replaces marginal coal fired stations, because their effects outweigh environmental hazards associated with incineration. However, there is a strong argument for comparing incineration with the new 'long run' marginal power stations that will have to be built in the UK over the next decade, which are likely to be either nuclear or renewable energy sources. On this basis, incineration would remain with a negative impact, comparable to landfill. Even on the coal fired basis, incineration has one-tenth of the environmental impact of recycling.

38. At modest levels (an average basket of recyclables at £25 a tonne, packaging

subsidies at £20 a tonne and zero recycling credits since we are considering system costs) the overall income covered less than a quarter of system collection and processing costs.

39. The high diversion system in Quinte, Ontario cut waste management system costs by 30 per cent. See Blue Box 2000, 1996.

40. For some of the difficulties in restructuring the energy sector see: Weizsacker, Lovins and Lovins, *Factor Four*, op cit, part II, and Michael Best, *Power to Compete, A Study of the Electrical Power Industry and Industrial Competitiveness in America and New England, Center for Industrial Competitiveness*, University of Massachusetts Lower, 1997.

41. When the London Planning Advisory Committee put forward their plan for 70 per cent recycling and composting, which had unanimous cross-party support from all borough planning members, this was opposed by officers from all four waste disposal authorities, and by most of the members on those authorities. The member majority on the West London Waste Authority were the only ones to place a moratorium on incineration: the others are planning for its expansion. This is the general pattern and it has made an integrated strategy led by the collection authorities centred on intensive 'diversion' and co-ordinated facilities much harder to achieve.

42. The recent Surrey contract includes incineration capacity for 67 per cent of available municipal waste, recycling capacity for 15 per cent, supplemented by sub-contracted composting and residual landfill. This is similar to Cleveland, to the North East London Waste Disposal Authority (containing Edmonton), Lewisham and Greenwich (who promot-

ed SELCHP), and Sheffield.

43. DETR, *Less Waste More Value*, HMSO, 1998.

44. *Materials Recycling Weekly*, 21 May 1999.

45. The body regulating the administration of the offset scheme estimates that 50 per cent of the spending under the scheme has the 10 per cent contribution funded by third parties.

46. One of the concessions achieved by the waste industry during the establishment of the scheme was that they should be allowed to use their logos and names on environmental body literature.

47. 'Landfill tax and the pitfalls of privatised public spending' *ENDS Report* 289, February 1999, which reviews the first two years of the scheme.

48. For a review of outcome taxes in waste and waste taxes more generally, see T Bernheim, *Economic Instruments in Waste Management*, Association of Cities for Recycling, Brussels, July 1998.

49. PRNs conform to the theory of money that defines money as anything which the state will accept in payment of its debts. See GF Knapp, *The State Theory of Money*, London 1924.

50. For the latest data on the performance of the packaging scheme see DETR, *Increasing Recovery and Recycling of Packaging Waste in the United Kingdom*, June 1999.

51. Where there is no excess demand for recycled materials, the value of PRNs will not feed back to the collectors of the material since the ordinary market is providing sufficient quantities. In the case of a shortage, a monopoly processor will have two alternatives: to increase supply by direct funding of incremental projects, so that existing projects receive

no increases in material revenues: or to raise material prices sufficient to expand supply, while at the same time taking a premium from the PRN price paid by the obligated parties. With a monopoly processor acting as broker, there is no direct way in which an increase in the price of PRNs will feed back to the material supply price. In the language of microeconomics, the processor will be able to capture substantial parts of the producer and consumer surplus.

52. DETR, *Increasing Recovery and Recycling of Packaging Waste*, opcit, p17.

53. For a survey of producer responsibility schemes see G Gies and J McGinnis, *Producer Responsibility and Local Authority Recycling Programmes*, London Pride Waste Action Programme, 1997. The Manitoba scheme provides support payments for every tonne of eligible materials, covering 80 per cent of the cost of the programmes. The Dutch programme operates similarly but at a lower level.

54. House of Commons, Environment, Transport and Regional Affairs Committee, Sixth Report, Sustainable Waste Management, Vol II, Minutes of Evidence, HC 484-II, June 1998, pp 92-3

55. Ulrich Beck's argument initially appeared in English in *Risk Society: Towards a New Modernity*, Sage 1992, and was followed by *Environmental Politics in an Age of Risk*, Polity 1995, the *Re-Invention of Politics*, Polity 1997, and a number of jointly authored works. See also Scott Lash et al (eds) *Risk, Environment and Modernity: Towards a New Ecology*, Sage 1996

56. Op cit, p95.

57. See Neil Stanley 'Public concern: the decision maker's dilemma', *Journal of Planning Law*, 1998, pp 919-934.

58. For a review of waste related cases see P Shiner, 'Environmental Protection, Judicial Review and Human Rights,' Judicial Review, March 1999.

59. The importance of localising decision making over waste disposal is brought out by the case of the Nant-Y-Gwyddon landfill in the Rhonda. There had been widespread local protests at the condition of the landfill. The local labour council defended the conduct of its LAWDAC, which managed the landfill. At the elections for the Welsh Assembly, the district council and the European Parliament, the condition of the landfill site and Plaid Cymru's commitment to close it was a major factor in Plaid's successive victories over Labour .

60. Another body to adopt a zero discharge strategy is the US/Canadian International Joint Commission on the Great Lakes. They set this goal in part through a rejection of the idea of 'safe levels' of assimilation of certain toxic substances. 'The idea of non-zero assimilitative capacity in the environment and in our bodies (and hence allowable discharges) for some chemicals is no longer relevant.' Accordingly their aim is to control inputs of 'persistent toxic substances that will leads to their virtual elimination'. See Seventh Biannual Report, 1993.

References for box on page 73:
Biocycle, 'Recycling Manufacturing Zone Proposal', July 1993; Clean Washington Center, *Notes on Economic Impacts*, 1997; Lewis M, *Recycling Economic Development through Scrap Based Manufacturing*, Institute for Local Self Reliance, 1994; Minnesota Office of Environmental Assessment, *Minnesota's Value Added Recycling Manufacturing Industries*, (520

Lafayette Road North, St Paul, Minn, 55155-4100), 1997; Morris, D and Seldman, N, *Recycling as Economic Development*, Institute for Local Self Reliance, 1993; O'Hara, F, *Recycling and the Maine Economy* (nd); Platt,B, Jeanes,H, and Kaufmann A, *Recycling Means Business in Baltimore, DC and Richmond*, Institute for Self Reliance, 1995; Seattle Solid Waste Utility, *Recycling Potential Assessment*, 1994; Touart, A.P. 'Life and Times of Clean Washington Center: Lessons in Market Development' Biocycle, July 1997; Weston, RF Inc, *Value Added to Recyclable Materials in the North East*, North East Recycling Council, US, May 1994.